THE INNER ROAD TO WISDOM AND HEALING

THE INNER ROAD TO WISDOM AND HEALING

Writing My Way to Health

Carol Ann Deans

Book Guild Publishing
Sussex, England

First published in Great Britain in 2012 by
The Book Guild Ltd
Pavilion View
19 New Road
Brighton, BN1 1UF

Typesetting in Garamond by
Nat-Type, Cheshire

Printed and bound in Great Britain by
CPI Group (UK) Ltd, Croydon, CR0 4YY

A catalogue record for this book is available from
The British Library.

ISBN 978 1 84624 749 1

Dedicated with love to my husband Alan
and
To all sufferers of chronic ailments
and those who care for them

Acknowledgements

With huge thanks to Kurt Abraham, whose gentle encouragement made this book possible; Alistair Paterson for reading an earlier draft and giving very useful suggestions; Sandy Ferguson and Avril and Maury Toshner, the very finest of friends who not only sheltered and fed me, but cared for me, always; Dr. Maureen Lockhart and Linda Evans, selfless healing colleagues and friends; my family and other fine friends who didn't abandon me even through the difficult times; and finally, Bradley, Clare and Jacob for enriching my life, Love you all!

Preface

It was nearing morning and I was in bed, in that lovely space of not being quite asleep, but warm and comfortable and conscious enough to be enjoying it, when suddenly the space inside my head cleared then filled with beautiful colour. Wow! I thought. That's nice. Still feeling quiet and cosy, my inner screen was completely filled with a huge, glorious blue eye. I could see every little detail and, though eyes are not my favourite thing to scrutinize, I was fascinated by every vein and variation. It was mounted on a wooden stand as if it was an exhibit in a glass case and the stand slowly started to turn showing me all of the eye, front and back. The colour was so astonishing and the details so clear that I was too fascinated to be squeamish!

The picture then changed seamlessly from the blue eye to a fish. I could see every detail of every scale of iridescent blue/green, its fins, gills and tail, even the little red streaks in its eyes with silver/grey around the rims. It was on a similar wooden stand, which again started to turn slowly so it could be viewed from every angle. It was stunning and the colours stay with me still.

Again the picture changed; this time becoming a scene. It looked like a small town and I was reminded of old cowboy pictures with shops on raised wooden sidewalks. Then people started to appear, walking up and down the wooden verandas and I was aware that sound was audible too. The scene became quite animated with people, colour and noise. I was having a lovely time observing and 'wowing'.

Next, I was in a car which was moving through the countryside. I could see greenery and hedgerows as the car sped on its way.

"Fantastic!" I said. "I want to drive." I took the steering wheel feeling very pleased with myself, but as I did so the noise faded, the colour faded, the car disappeared and I was back in my bed, back to reality.

1

Did I say back to *reality?* These shifting sands? This 'Moveable Famine' (if I may misquote Ernest Hemingway)? In my former *reality* how often I would sigh and say, "Oh, if only I could have a few months' rest, some quiet time to myself, read some books."

The words 'Be careful what you wish for' spring to mind. The longed-for 'few months' rest' became years. 'Some quiet time to myself' turned into isolation, loneliness and pain. I did get to read a lot of books though and slowly a new life unfolded. In fact, my Blue Eye experience played a significant part in this unfolding, but it required some contemplation. I had been so excited to take the wheel, but why did it suddenly stop? It felt like as soon as I wanted to be the one in charge the magic went. First lesson to be learned? Give up control. Enjoy the ride. Submit.

Submitting I am not so good at and I am reminded of how, when we were kids, my brother and I would fight and it usually ended with him getting the better of me, pinning me to the floor and either bashing or tickling me.

"Do you capitulate?" he would say, bash, tickle and I would always reply, "NEVER!"

But back to my visions; as good fortune would have it, that same day, I had been invited to my first healers get-together in the home of a lady who was hosting an afternoon of sharing and encouragement for both new and experienced healers. I was excited that I was able to share my experience with people who might understand and when I did, it was met with an attitude of, 'Well, that was very nice but it was just your third eye opening.'

As the meeting went on, I realized that something had also happened to my ability to sense. Our hostess showed us the site of an old well in her garden and as I walked towards it I bumped into something like a cartoon character bumping into a pane of glass and bounced backwards, but there was nothing there. Bewildered, I tried again. Bump, bounce. Huh! The others just laughed. I had obviously met the energy field of the well. Also in the garden was a handsome old tree and some of the group were sheltering under its boughs, as it was a rare hot and sunny day in Scotland. I made to join them, got to within about three feet of the tree and, again, the invisible pane of glass, bump and bounce. This time, though, I felt stuck to the energy field and had to be prised off by a friendly 'earthed' healer.

As the home of our hostess was at the seaside, I walked to the shore after the group disbanded, bought an ice-cream and contemplated my day. I felt absolutely thrilled though slightly concerned about invisible energy fields!

A couple of weeks earlier I had been on a training course for spiritual healers in Edinburgh, with the National Federation of Spiritual Healers. It was quite a surprise to find myself there as I don't remember how I even knew there was such a thing, but once there I felt compelled to know more. Someone else was definitely pulling the strings. However, this was the start of my life changing forever. I felt as if I had been too long out in the cold and, rushing back, I threw open the door and shouted, "I'm home, Mum!" I felt safe, warm and understood by the new people I met there and I received help, healing, counselling and encouragement, as well as experiencing my first lessons in training to be a spiritual healer. The National Federation of Spiritual Healers, I was to learn, is a large, highly regarded organization, which is non-denominational, with good training and a strict code of conduct.

Why healing? Good question, because no one was more surprised by this change of direction than me, but let me backtrack a bit for some edited highlights.

I had been struggling with poor health. My mother died. I had two recent damaging relationships with unsuitable men. Divorced for many years, I was bringing up my son alone. He was now in his early teens and was, shall we say, difficult. I worked a full day and collapsed early in the evening, often sleeping entire weekends.

My home was undergoing major rebuilding works and we had to move out for an estimated time of at least two years. The alternative housing offered by the local authority was not really to our taste and my son and I were united in agreement over the barbed wire around the windows. *No likey!* We threw ourselves on the mercy of my dear friend Sandy and together with the two cats, my son and I moved into his very small flat. Wall climbing space was at a premium.

I had a new man in my life offering happy diversions and the possibility of a brighter future, but I seemed hell-bent on a collision course and pushed through fatigue to qualify as a reflexologist (in my spare time!) and did I mention I changed my job? I started working for a fascist: the kind of man who rubbed his hands in glee when there was someone to fire – Mussolini with hair!

My son was expelled from school, ran away from home and generally was, shall we say, very difficult. My health grew worse. Mussolini wanted me to be gone as I was proving unreliable due to my poor health. Did I capitulate? Never! Well, not until one morning, feeling more nauseous with fatigue than usual, I got out of bed to go to work and fell on the floor – a complete crumple. Thereafter, unable to move or wipe the dribble from my mouth, I lay in bed, a little bit fascinated with all the weird things happening to my body. I assumed I was dying, but I could not have cared less. Lost my job, lost my new man, lost the ability to look after myself, had no home or money. What was the problem with dying? Some dear friends thought differently and for many months thereafter they cared for me in their beautiful and tranquil home.

While staying with these friends a therapist visited and I was tested for allergies using Applied Kinesiology, or muscle response, which was very interesting. She then offered me healing and although I did not know what she meant, I agreed. As I lay in bed she sat by my side and held my hand. So far so good. Then she said, "What does your illness look like?" *Huh!* I thought. *What does it look like? Is she mad?* But, suddenly a malignant little face floated up before me, all grey and spiky: a little bit like Mr. Messy in the *Mr. Men* books but really horrid. Its nasty screechy voice said to me, "You're useless! Useless! Useless!"

"Am not!" I replied like a petulant child.

"Useless, useless, useless!" the evil little Brillo Pad face jeered.

I started to cry. I tried in vain to stick up for myself, but instead I howled, then realized I was agreeing with him. Useless. Yes, quite right. I *was* useless. I was a failed everything: failed wife and mother; no job; new lover gone; no home – useless!

I cried for a long time, but I began to realize that here was where I had to start to help myself be well. I needed to learn to heal myself, to forgive myself. The journey started right there.

2

Eventually, I was back in my flat attempting to take responsibility for myself and my son, but life was not easy. I was not able to do very much. I was, at first, not even able to leave the flat at all, but gradually, some days, I could go out once in the day. My flat was on the third floor of a Glasgow tenement and my legs screamed 'Waw! Waw! Waw!' all the climb back up the stairs, so I had to plan carefully any forays into the greater world.

My son said he "hates me for being sick. Hates me!" His behaviour was growing worse and my screeching responses growing screechier. It was a horrible cycle. Everything between us felt broken and each upset or quarrel or imagined slight would have me doubled over in pain.

Isolation and loneliness brought their own quality of pain, which, in me, dwelt in the very centre of my body, my middle, my stomach: the area I learned was called the Solar Plexus. This is the seat of the emotions and mine felt very damaged.

Surprisingly, I was not depressed. I felt determined to dedicate myself to being well and understanding the problem that had been diagnosed as M.E. But I had my work cut out for me. I read books on health, spirituality, healing, nutrition and, in fact, while seeking out suitable books on these subjects I answered an advertisement placed by someone who was selling a collection of such books. Strange old chap – he subjected me to an interrogation on the telephone before even granting an interview to view the books. When I was finally permitted to see them I bought some on diet, health and yoga breathing techniques. He wanted to know why I was interested in these subjects and when I explained he told me about Nature Cure and about the old Kingston Clinic in Edinburgh. It had been started by the pioneer, James C Thomson, in 1938 and until 1988 was a residential clinic. It was considered quite cooky by the mainstream, but changed the lives of many many people. It taught that the power of healing is found in nature and that everyone should take responsibility for maintaining their own health. Although the clinic was now closed, he encouraged me to make an appointment with Alec Milne who still practised Nature Cure and visited Glasgow every week to see clients, which I did.

Meeting him was an absolute joy and such a contrast to the 'support' that I had previously received. Up until that point the advice had been very scholarly and serious, imposing strict guidelines on lifestyle and diet. It was all, "Oh no, you can't eat that," or "Oh no, better not go there. I wouldn't try that," etc. And then there was the, "Have an early night," or "You just need a holiday," kind of advice, which was usually accompanied by a pat on the back and a supercilious smile. M.E. was still not understood or even accepted as being a real illness, so I realize that these professionals were doing their best, but it was all so negative. So, when I met Alec Milne and Nature Cure, it was a joy to hear him say, "If you like to do it, do it. If it is life-enhancing and makes you feel good, go right ahead."

My spirits really lifted and although there was a regime to follow, it felt full of optimism.

In Nature Cure the day starts with a dip in a cold bath. I did this every morning without fail and after a few months I could do it without using very foul language. After even more months I would feel out of sorts if I missed my daily dip. It just leaves you feeling glowing, warm, frisky and your skin is soft and taut. Honest!

Then comes fresh fruit for breakfast and a morning walk is recommended, although my once-a-day down the stairs rule did not always allow me to do this. Salad for lunch with a small piece of cheese follows and for dinner some cooked veg (a small piece of meat is usual, but as I am now a vegetarian I miss out on that). A cup of tea is permitted in the afternoon, but strictly no coffee.

After just a short time of sticking to the regime I felt a real boost and started to feel more on an even keel. I was able to spend time studying the recommended books on my trainee healer's list and discovered groups, such as Psychical Research and Dowsers, which I attended whenever I could. My physical world had vastly shrunk, but the world inside my head was expanding all the time. In fact, my new spiritual awakening left a cosy warm place, like a secret love in my heart. I smiled a lot. I felt sore and ill and weak, but I also felt blessed – corny, I know, but true. My new found facets of myself and the knowledge I felt I was gaining sustained me through those first few years.

As I grew in confidence, I began to practise the creative visualization and relaxation techniques I had learned about, first of all using music to help transport myself to different worlds, but eventually preferring silence to meditate in. There is huge mystique around meditation, which is really unnecessary as the goal is to quieten the mind and watch this space. Sai Baba says that the spiritual journey is just like a car journey: "Start early, go slowly and arrive safely." And so it is with meditation in my view. Don't try anything fancy, don't push or force yourself and all will unfold.

Another saying I came across was, "Enlightenment is an accident. Meditation makes you accident-prone." For sure, the more I practise stilling my mind, the easier it becomes, but my goal of remaining in that peaceful state is shattered before long.

It is a new year, but it does not start well. My dear dad dies.

I discover in my grief that I have not finished grieving for my mother and I am overwhelmed. Then, my son, aged 16, packs a bag and leaves – the worst day of my life. Another crumple and I lie on the floor in the foetal position till long after the sun sets on that awful day. Worry, grief and anxiety plague me and M.E. lays me low, very low.

In an attempt to make sense of things, I laboriously record my dreams. Don't worry, I am not about to bore you rigid; just to say that these were definitely stress dreams – lots of conflict, lost in underground tunnels, dark lanes, running, confused and very very afraid; out of control, out of my control, elevators out of control; running, running always running, but I also started flying, which was fun. Sometimes there were golden-haired babies, but most of all toilets – always looking for, but never being able to use – and someone would always be looking at me. Once, after searching a long time for a toilet, I found one in a bar. I sat on the toilet and then realized that there was a window from the lounge bar that looked right into the toilet. Two men were watching me and I got so annoyed, I shouted to them, "Put your heads in and have a good look." When one man did, I slapped him and punched him on the nose. Now, that felt better.

My dreams had also become Technicolor. I saw wonderful scenes from Barnum and Bailey-type circuses, red white and blue, silver stars and golden fountains and I so looked forward to sleep – like going to the Odeon without the popcorn. The more my life lacked in action the more jam-packed and colourful my dream life became. A blessed compensation.

Around this time I had a dream – or was I awake? The scene was of people and nature but everything was dark, colourless and ugly. The people were square, coarse and unattractive. Gradually the scene became prettier, lighter and the people more refined. It seemed that they were evolving.

They were refusing to eat meat. *How wonderful,* I thought, *the people are starting to care.*

Then a voice said, "This is your first glimpse of paradise." I felt awake, not dreaming and heard myself saying, "Wow!" at the lovely and lush pictures.

My now passionate interest in spiritual healing was the most exciting thing for me and I imagined a swift and perfect healing for myself, followed by a career of healing others. My reputation would be legend! But although I was able to read, meditate and develop inwardly as a spiritual healer, my ability to work in the physical was still restricted. It was only after three years of training and self-development that I felt OK about calling myself a healer. I knew that this entailed a lifetime of learning and discovery and this thrilled me. I would never, ever be bored.

December 1994, I had a dream in which I was in the company of a minister who was saying very interesting things. He didn't seem like the usual sort of church minister and I was listening attentively. I asked him if he believed in reincarnation, karma and healing. He said, "of course". As if to prove this, he led me to a house where a young man with a damaged knee was sitting on the doorstep. The minister then called upon the Spirit of White Eagle to come and heal the young man's knee. Instantly, he was there with his hands on the young man's knee and it was healed. After this, I felt that the Spirit of White Eagle was to be my healing guide and when I plucked up the courage to ask him if this was so, he turned to me and replied that not everyone, especially women, could get on with him. He said that persons tended to be thinner with an 'inner hunger'. I wasn't quite sure what that meant. Then I was shown a huge book, full of rules that I had to keep. I said I didn't care about the rules; I could cope if he would be my guide. He then appeared to me in the form of an old man, tall and thin with white hair parted in the middle and a headband holding a single white feather. He seemed to be wearing a breastplate, perhaps made of bone and a kind of apron (I don't know the words to describe his Native American form of dress). He had a smooth and serene face. I woke up feeling very good about this and very excited.

This is me, I think, *on my way.*

3

Back to earth with a thump. Here's how it goes: one day I'm
fine, next day I wake feeling beaten up and overhung. Whoa!
Did I not sleep? Was I partying all night long? No. My old
'friend' M.E. is calling. Legs wobbly, bad-tempered, nauseous;
I feel as if I've been in a road accident. I am exhausted but I
am restless. My scalp feels as if it has been grated. My eyes
burn. I hate everybody – just leave me alone. Go on, bugger
off! Cancel the day, the week, the month. Who knows how
long. Again. And, why is this the day when the dogs bark
more than usual, the neighbours' noise is unbearable,
electrical things break, bad news arrives. Why do the planets
crash and hurtle towards me, crush me, suffocate me, pin me
down (image of brother pinning me to the ground – do I
capitulate – Yes, I bloody well do!!) Leave me alone. I am a
good person. I try very hard to be a good person. Why oh
why? What's the use of why oh why? I hurtle even faster into
the deep dark place if I struggle and question.

Is there a difference between letting go and submitting?
Let Go
Submit
Surrender
Capitulate

When is it positive and when is it negative? When to be
cowardly and when to be courageous? When to the light,
when to the dark? Surrender to Jesus. Submit to the Devil.
Capitulate to the enemy. Let go of the struggle. Let go, let

God. Lie back and think of Scotland. Lie down and die. Pick a card, any card.

Do I feel better for ranting and raving? Depends. I can use a great deal of bad language, wear myself out with anger and tears before calming down, taking a big breath, dusting myself off and starting all over again. But I am particularly adept at finding the smallest life raft to cling to: an unexpected phone call from a friend; a little bird singing (a favourite of mine); a ray of sunshine (physical or metaphoric). I can wallow in an ocean of misery and still find a teeny weeny bit of flotsam to save me. But it was my desire to be well, to heal myself, that really drove me on. It was still strong and the belief that I would also be able to help others kept me going.

My First Client

A young woman comes to me for healing. She is not very informative about what ails her, but that's ok. The peace descends and the healing begins. Her shoulders relax and I feel it's all going according to instruction. However, she starts to softly cry, then loudly. Wailing and howling follow and I am beginning to think about the neighbours. The room is getting dark as time goes on and it's evening now and still she howls and is giving someone a piece of her mind. Eventually, in the gloom of our surroundings, she starts to slow to a sob and a blub then she takes some sharp breaths and at last she's done. She stands up, smiles, blows her nose one last time and says, "Thanks, that was brilliant," and takes her leave full of beans. Me? Well, I was completely wiped out and traumatized. I had felt so useless. I didn't know what to say or do. I just sat beside her, occasionally pressing a dry tissue into her hand and chastising myself for being useless. (Oh oh! In comes useless again – get out of here! I did my best.) I resolved to find out what I should have done and discovered the Foundation for Emotional Therapy where I undertook training to help me delve deeper and really understand human emotions. It was phenomenal. I learned that emotions are neither good nor bad. They just are. I learned to let go of loads of my stuff and how to continually do that. I became braver at facing the emotions of others and I also discovered that really I had done the right thing with my crying client. I allowed her the safe space to have a good clear out. The healing energy helped release and I allowed her to keep going. What a system! I also learned that this was to be the direction for my healing work. I was working on the emotional level as opposed to the denser physical level; in so doing, I was learning to understand and help myself be more open and trusting and also more loving toward myself. I had to learn to let go in order to convince others to do the same.

Another fantastic discovery was the concept of archetypes. Very Jungian, but I found them very easy to use. The most obvious is the Archetypal Mother and, as part of my training, I was led on a journey to meet my spiritual parents by Sheila Ward, our teacher. Sheila was a pioneer in this field and, I believe, responsible for setting up the foundation.

I was very resistant to the idea of Spiritual Mother. My mum had died a few years earlier and I felt hugely loyal to her, indignant at any hint of her not being sufficient. I loved her very much, but Sheila explained that it was not about replacing the parents we had. It was about having extra help on spiritual realms for anything that the inner child felt had been lacking. So, still resisting, Sheila led me in a creative visualization through a lovely garden, where I admired the colours of the flowers, listened to birdsong, felt the breeze on my face and the springy grass under my feet. I walked further into a meadow where at last I sat under a huge old oak tree and allowed the warmth of the sun to relax me even more. Sheila told me to imagine myself as a little child and then to look down at my hands on the grass – and, yes, they were the hands of a child. I felt relaxed and sleepy and after a while I noticed a man walking towards me. He wore a cap and a suit of rough cloth and his name was John. He seemed to be a gamekeeper and was going into the woods on his rounds, seeing that everything was as it should be.

"Can I come too?" asked my little child.

Without hesitation, he replied, "Yes."

I skipped happily alongside him. Sometimes he held my hand, sometimes I ran and tumbled, but all the time I chattered. "What's this? What do you call that?" And he answered patiently and with good humour. I felt very happy and, after a while, 'I' on the outside, as watcher, had the insight that John was really listening to me. I had his full attention and I realized for the first time that, as a child, I was never listened to! My dad in the real world was a lovely gentle man, but not truly present. I have dear memories of him sitting, dreaming, smoking his pipe, and me sitting at his feet while he stroked my hair. I loved his touch and I loved him, but I believe I was interchangeable with the family dog. I would chatter and he would nod.

My mum was a wonderful housekeeper and cook, and worked miracles with the housekeeping purse, but there was never any energy for me – just for me alone. Not when I was a child.

As these realizations unfolded on my first meeting with John, I found myself sobbing and feeling very sorry for my little child. He held me and let me pour it all out and I had such a sense of non-judgemental presence. I hadn't before appreciated that this had been missing in my life, but now that I had, I had a lot to think about and connections to make. I eventually said goodbye to John and asked if I could see him again the next day. He agreed and that was the start of a beautiful relationship. I met him daily, confided feelings I had never before allowed to surface, like the times I had felt hurt or let down or misjudged – pure feeling, not logic or grown up understanding. I told John all the things I would have felt disloyal or ashamed to tell a 'real' person and I came to many understandings of why I reacted the way I did to certain things, why I felt needy of certain things. In fact, I was beginning to see ME.

After a few meetings, one day John took me to his home to meet his wife – I suppose my Spiritual Mother. She was a fulsome woman with a huge squashy bosom: an archetypal cuddly mum. She was busy baking, her apron covered in flour and the smell of warm cakes wafted out of the range. She was full of laughter with a heart that was as big as her bosom and I wanted to be held there. I wanted her arms around me to shut out the world, shut out all the hurts and the pain and enfold me in her warm soft squashy love.

I am still the child. I always will be, and when it gets too much I go to her. I just turn up. The welcome is always warm. There is always smoke coming out of the chimney and something good bubbling or baking. My Spiritual Mother has open arms and an open heart and enfolds my 'child' unquestioningly.

Clarissa Pinkola Estes, author of the wonderful *Women Who Run with the Wolves*, writes that she often told her daughters, "You are born to one mother, but if you are lucky, you will have more than one and among them all you will find most of what you need."

I understand what she means. I love my mum and cherish her memory and realize that because of my loyalty to her I would never have allowed anyone else to mother me. The meetings with my Spiritual Parents, however, gave me so much that I wanted my mum and dad to enjoy this too. So I decided to take them on a journey to the woods with me.

Before sitting quietly, I took out some old photographs so that I could have a very clear picture of them as little children. My heart melted as I looked into their faces. Once I had them clearly in my mind's eye, I began the journey with my parents accompanying me.

Now, there was not a dry eye in the house. I allowed my dad to tell his story and cry over his hurts. I saw his inner child unfold as it all poured out of him. Same with my mum. Poor, poor things. They needed love too. They needed their stories listened to. They were only children themselves, full of love and longing and spaces never filled, tears never wiped and sores never kissed.

I know that my childhood was a good one and that my experiences and my hurts are nothing compared to the stories of others, but Spiritual Parents are there for everyone, with limitless love and patience until the end of our days, and our stories are eventually told.

Sheila Ward also introduced me to the concept of using writing as therapy, as catharsis, and I have gratefully integrated this into my life.

4

My training with the Foundation for Emotional Therapy took place in Kirkby Fleetham Hall in North Yorkshire. It was a beautiful house set in lovely grounds with its own lake. Swans and ducks too. It also had an old Norman church complete with sarcophagi of Knights Templar. Originally, the village had been in these same grounds, but one of the owners had decided that the locals were just too close and the village was moved further away. The house, which at one time was burnt down and rebuilt, has an amazing history, full of stories of Jacobite plots being hatched, hangings gone wrong leaving lop-sided ghosts to roam the halls, visits from King William and Queen Mary and then there was lost treasure, still never found. I had stayed there often and always had lovely experiences and dreams there. However, one of the training sessions was taking place in the winter and another trainee, like myself, had arrived the evening before. The house was huge and there had been no other courses or workshops held there for a while so it was very, very cold. Even one day of unnecessary heating cost a fortune, so Helen, the other trainee, and I were staying in a wing of the house next to the sitting room where the sessions would be held. It had a huge open fire and we had plenty of logs, so we huddled there till bedtime.

Had we been telling ghost stories? I don't know, but Helen was definitely spooked and did not want to close the door of her bedroom, which was opposite mine. Me? Well, I was so cold there was no way I was leaving my door open, come what may. Two duvets covered my body, my ears and my head. Boy, it was Baltic. It was also completely dark. Pitch-black. I fell asleep easily, half-suffocated by duvets, but some time later was awakened by the sound of furniture being moved in the sitting room. I thought, *It's still dark; why is the furniture being moved now?* But more loud scrapes and scuffs and bumps followed. Eventually, I turned on the light to look at my watch which said 3 a.m.

Very strange, I thought and put out the light and listened, wondering if I should go and look. But on top of fearing I might freeze to death, I didn't really feel that brave. I slept again then woke to the sound of heavy feet climbing steps above my room. It took a moment or two to remember there was nothing above my room! Then, I heard a bell ringing, an ancient knoll sounding as if the noise was muffled through fog – a warning from a village church perhaps. What a night.

I had forgotten to bring an alarm clock, so I told my brain to wake me at 8 a.m. as classes started promptly. It was still dark when a helluva racket from the ducks, right outside my window, woke me at exactly 8 a.m.

Helen heard absolutely nothing of the ghostly goings-on. When I told Sheila, our trainer, however, she said, "Oh, that's because it's been so cold and *they* like to come in for heat. It will be quieter tonight once they are warmed up."

Strangely enough, it was.

Discovering Different Energies

Chanting. Now that's a powerful thing. Again at Kirkby Fleetham Hall, I was taking part in a workshop with Julie Soskin, an accomplished workshop facilitator as well as an author, medium and teacher.

It had been an exciting morning of different meditation techniques and chanting, but as I chanted I felt my auric space grow and grow like Topsy. By the end of the session, as we stood up to leave the room, I suddenly thought, *Nope. No way am I going to get through that door.*

I staggered to the left and staggered to the right with the weight of this enormous aura. I stood as if on the deck of a ship in a turbulent sea, feet planted wide apart, arms outstretched as I tried not to wobble. I waited till everyone else had left then I made a run for the door.

"Whooee! Made it!"

Now I had to go to my room as my skin was on fire. I felt like a sausage in a hot pan – if my skin was pricked I would burst. My very pink body sizzled as I lowered it into a cool bath where I remained till I felt more normal.

As I learned more about energy and energy fields, my consciousness was opening to all sorts of different possibilities, such as, when walking in the gardens of Kirkby Fleetham Hall that same weekend, I bent down and smiled at some small, white, bell-shaped flowers that had large glossy leaves. I think they were Lily of the Valley. I caressed a little flower and said, "Aren't you lovely," and I was rewarded and greatly surprised by tinkling laughter. I couldn't see anything so I politely enquired, "Excuse me, are you fairies?" The infectious giggling grew and I had a mental picture of them rolling around, kicking their little legs in great hilarity. I felt no doubt that they were indeed fairies and I gave myself over to joyful laughter, proclaiming, "I do believe in fairies," like an excited child at the pantomime. Fortunately, no one nearby looked askance at my outburst as it seemed that magical moments were being enjoyed all around.

This expansion of consciousness answered a puzzling experience I had had a few years earlier with my cat, Dusty, who was a little scrap of a thing with a huge personality. Here is what happened:

The weather had been very strange: heavy and hot and

thundery. I didn't feel so good. My chest felt tight and I was quite breathless and tired and headachey. My flat felt airless, but I didn't want to open the windows too wide in case Dusty went walkabout. A good storm would have cleared the air and it became more and more difficult to get a good breath. I was alone in my flat and I lay on top of the bed hoping for a breeze, but the night became heavier and heavier.

I started to get a little concerned as my airways felt on fire then they felt as if they were closing altogether. Dusty was beside me. I felt very lightheaded and must have passed out as when I came to, Dusty was on the pillow, pressing down on the crown of my head and purring like a little dynamo. It quickly crossed my mind that this was no time for silly games, but I blacked out again. When I came to, I found myself at the window, then at the front door trying to suck air from under the door. I was flapping about on the floor like a newly-landed fish, losing consciousness, then finding myself in a different part of the flat, but always with Dusty either sitting on my head or my upper chest, purring, purring, purring.

I was unable to seek help. I was not afraid, but survival instinct had taken over. I strained and flapped and flailed. I clawed at the air, trying to grasp what I needed in my hands. One more breath, just one more breath. I didn't expect to see the morning. I remember feeling sorrow for my son and my mother, and so grateful for the loving presence of my little cat. When the dawn broke, however, I was still alive and it really was a new day. How to explain that shiny, other-worldly, peaceful gratitude? How to explain Dusty?

Now that I had more experience of chakras and energy fields, it makes sense to me that Dusty instinctively knew what to do, keeping my life force active through my crown chakra and my heart with the power of her own purring, dynamic life force.

There are humans who heal animals, but there are also

animals known to calm and soothe humans, as well as alerting them to danger and keeping them safe. There are numerous accounts of strong psychic links between humans and their pets, but I haven't heard of any other animal actually keeping a human breathing.

Learning More About White Eagle

Meanwhile, Spirit of White Eagle, as so often, is there waiting for me in my meditations. He stands tall and patient, hands folded over his chest. When at times my mind wanders, I rush back and apologize. He doesn't scold. He shows me – sit with ankles crossed (if not able to sit cross-legged on the ground). This has the effect of opening out the body so that the chakras are open and receptive. He teaches me to sit and listen in this receptive pose. He tells me this is respectful to the teacher and shows you are listening and taking in his wisdom. Even if one does not understand the words, the wisdom can still be received through the energy centres.

There is a difference in the quality of my healing energy when I call on Spirit of White Eagle to be with me. I feel more confident as I feel his presence standing at my back, but our relationship can be extremely challenging.

One day, for instance, going into my meditation, I am feeling rebellious. He always stands waiting for me, so serene and patient, but I don't feel warmth or sympathy. When I am feeling unwell and sorry for myself and looking for some solace he always says, "You must stand tall."

And so I say, "Why are you always so strict? Other people have loving, soft Spirit Guides."

He replies, "I have to be strict. You are attached to will and so am I. You Must Stand Tall!"

"Ok," I sigh. "I'll try." And I do.

I had started meeting with a couple of other women who

were also interested in meditation and channelling and one of them looked at me, sitting openly with ankles crossed, and said, "Oh! Are you a member of The White Eagle Lodge?"

I hadn't heard of them and she explained that the way I was sitting was how it was taught to the members of the lodge. Ah ha! So that's who White Eagle is. Didn't know that. I investigated this and started reading White Eagle's books containing his lovely, gentle philosophy.

For almost two years Spirit of White Eagle's presence was with me and during that time I had many crises. I had sold my flat and moved in with my lover. However, my new spiritual passions did not sit well with him and we parted shortly after, got back together again for a while, then parted once more for what seemed like the final break.

It was also the beginning of many new adventures.

5

I had met a wonderful lady at a Nature Cure retreat who proved to be a big influence on my life. Her name was Grisel Stanley and she was remarkable. She had been a vegetarian all of her life and a very early advocate of homoeopathy and healing. She had opened a centre in England for homoeopathy and healing plus conventional care, called The Priory, long before these things were acceptable or popular. She ran this successfully until she and her husband moved to Scotland.

Shortly after we had met, she invited me to her very beautiful home in Moniaive, Dumfriesshire, where she held regular meditation and healing meetings in the old stable block. I visited her often after that and made friends in the area. So, when my lover and I parted, I fled to Grisel for comfort and a roof over my head and moved into The Stables. This was the start of a very active 'inner time' in my life and I had many adventures and some ghostly experiences there. It was very isolated and very dark. In fact, it was the ideal place to be alone and release all the emotions that needed to be released.

Meditation – Meeting the Wisdom Teacher

One day, while walking in the gardens, I felt urgently that I had to meditate. I rushed back to The Stables and put on rainforest music, which I felt very impressed to do, and quickly sat to meditate. I was immediately transported to a forest and felt myself running. I could hear the pounding of feet and saw small brown men running alongside me. There was a feeling of speed and urgency though not fear. When we came to a clearing I met with Spirit of White Eagle who led me to a step pyramid (with a flat top, like a Mayan one. Not like an Egyptian pointed one) and we climbed to the top to what appeared to be a temple – Inca or Mayan.

Once inside, I met a man who had straight black hair and wore a white band around his forehead. He was wearing a long white robe trimmed with gold and had a most wonderful face – handsome and gentle. He tells me he is to teach me wisdom. I say, "Oh, thank you. That's what I want most of all."

He says, "But first you have to learn love. Then I will teach you wisdom."

We sit on a balcony outside the temple. Spirit of White Eagle sits on his right and I sit on his left. Below us all the people are singing and dancing and he says, "See, God sent you here to serve the people. You must love them all. The old people, the babies."

Phew! I could see that I had to open my heart more to everyone. Compassion had perhaps been lacking.

Thereafter, in my meditations, I felt as if Spirit of White Eagle was gradually withdrawing from me and that a new guide would be showing 'herself' to me. It felt like a soft, gentle, feminine energy – pink. I waited to see.

Another lesson: Love and compassion must be learned and practised before gaining the wisdom I seek.

Learning How to Listen

While staying in The Stables at Moniaive, Grisel had a houseguest called Peter Dewey who was the rector at

Gordonstoun School. He did a great deal of charitable work in Romania with the orphans and involved the boys of Gordonstoun School in this work. He was to give a talk in Grisel's house, which was to be followed by a healing service in the lovely chapel there. He was such an inspirational man and everyone left feeling that they wanted to do something to help. However, here comes my 'useless' again. "What can I do?" I felt useless and frustrated all over again.

Later, I sat in meditation, determined to stay there until I got some answers. Patiently I waited, keeping my mind as still as I could and suddenly I heard, inside me or outside me, these words:

"Distant healing. Powerful. You can touch the world. This is the way forward. So much healing needed. Send your light out into the world. Romanian children only one problem area, but why not start there? You can help. Everyone can help. Don't think you can do nothing. The light is seen and we add to that light. Humankind must lead the way and we will help. It is your choice, your free will. We are not far away. We are lightworkers, but not of the earth. We are the boosters. You ignite the spark and we fan the flames. Spread this feeling. Promote the silent work of sending out the light. There is a fellowship of lightworkers. You will not be alone. Encourage people to spend a few minutes visualizing light going out from their hearts. This will also help them find their own connection with Spirit. In helping others they will help themselves – find their own path and illuminate it for themselves. Their vibrations will be raised closer to Spirit and will be more easily helped to find their own reasons for being, which is so important for humankind today. It is important to have a reason. So many have not been able to find the silence to contact their reason to be and so life has no meaning for them. They can be helped by learning about the light and taking responsibility for their thoughts. Open to Spirit. Spirit is patiently waiting. Not so long ago you did not know your reason for being – now you do – to help others find their reason for being! A big task but you can do it and we are here to help. Just remember to ask us! You do sometimes forget to ask. Greetings. Try to make this connection regular."

Well, that was interesting. There is no doubt that living in The Stables was giving me the necessary ingredients for quiet contemplation and hopefully communication.

A couple of days later I feel great agitation and a pounding in my heart centre. I sit and ask what is happening and am told that the etheric space of my heart is being stretched and this is affecting the physical heart. It will quieten down and love will flow in and out more easily. I am told to beware of the ego and remember that nothing is done without Spirit. I must breathe into the heart centre and allow it to open. This also affects the throat centre, which must expand too. There must be love and creativity before wisdom is unfolded.

I hear the message clearly: "See with your heart. Listen with your heart. Expand your aura. Others will be influenced by your auric space."

As the days pass, I try to make my time for communication late in the evening before bedtime and before I am too tired. Often, if I am too tired, the words are short but always encouraging. I am always encouraged to stay excited about my path, to "concentrate on distant healing and strengthening the focus of your mind. Working anonymously is good for dealing with the ego. Practise visualizing clients and healing their ailments. Sharpen psychic sight. This will all help you in the future. Patience and persistence."

I also seem to be receiving encouragement to write. I am told how truthful words from the heart have a different aura. Words used stay around you in the ether and always words of love should be chosen. We have a responsibility to use words of truth and love. Simple words are best – ones with 'round auras'. These are very powerful tools. Also, "Write with love and respect and the words will flow for you."

A couple of weeks later I hear:

"Words, words, words. Concepts. Useful to get a feel of the concept. Words can mislead. You know when a concept feels right although words can be necessary to relay the concept to someone else. This is the secret – to relay the concept without misleading with the wrong choice of words. Go back to simplicity and choose words that illumine, not confuse: words that the layman will not be frightened off by. You have had experience of trying to understand the jargon of the power seekers, the show-offs. You have also had experience of those who are humble and use easy words to convey a complicated concept, thereby making it easy to understand. Develop the skill of using the 'right' words. More meditation is needed to unfold more concepts. The energy will be there to help you focus, so choose wisely what you focus on."

Are these words from inside me or outside me? These words are personally interesting but hardly earth-shattering. I ask myself if these words are heard because I am alone, in a dark and isolated place and I'm entertaining myself with fantasy. Believe me, I do ask myself, but I come to the conclusion that my feelings of communing with Spirit sustain me and nourish me and so what if the words are not high and mighty, of prophet or oracle status. They sometimes answer my immediate questions, or move me onwards on my journey of self-discovery and that's the important thing.

So many people are now undertaking the journey of self-discovery and I believe that each man/woman can know themselves as no other can. No psychologist or therapist will ever know our whole story, but, occasionally, we need help to unravel a knot in the subconscious, an issue we have buried deeply in self-defence perhaps, or one we just don't want to deal with. We can then uncover another layer of consciousness, another facet of our seemingly unlimited facets. But are we ever free of hang-ups or knots? Do we ever deal with all our issues? Is it only the enlightened who are finished with human frailties and complexities? As long as we are human and not enlightened we must be involved in multifarious relationships and activities, some of which mould us in a way we do not like, while some harm us, mentally or physically. We may be able to express these along the way (a step nearer enlightenment) or we may repress them to create another knot or obstacle. So, is this why so many seek counselling, psychotherapy, etc? Not just to help our 'human' relationships and enhance our happiness in the here and now, but to clear the path to enlightenment?

I see that all the assistance and guidance I have received has certainly helped me in my human issues, giving me further understanding of myself, letting go of old hurts and old ways of looking at things. In fact, it is a valuable lesson to constantly look at our attitudes, our ways of doing things to see if they are still valid. I see myself as smoother, freer, stronger and more able to move forward as a result of doing this.

There is no doubt that mankind in his nature and personality is complex and the paradox seems to be that the more enlightened the person, the simpler they become. The enlightened seek less from outside as they know it is all within. Life's vision is vast, but within reach. I sense how it can become simpler and simpler because everything is from the One, is the One – we are all One. We have everything we need to be happy; we have all the wisdom already within. If death is natural and nothing to fear, what is there to fear in life? If there is nothing to fear, why do we struggle? If we are all One, why do we fight and kill each other and not share our resources? We do make life complicated. Why do we do that? Is it the struggle that makes us strive to evolve? But, if man is too busy struggling how can he even see that there is such a thing as enlightenment? If, for example, a man or woman is caught up in a struggle, such as a war zone, or they are refugees trying to feed their children, would the thought that this is part of their evolution make them furious? Is enlightenment a luxury some cannot afford to think about? At what stage in our evolution are we ready to seek the possibility of enlightenment and how many lifetimes will this take?

If I am to believe those that 'see' then I am a very old soul. I have had many past lives as priests and priestesses, in the temples, etc. and yet here I am, still struggling and ignorant and looking for answers and pointers to the path of light. Is enlightenment the result of laziness or of great suffering and experience? Will I even recognize enlightenment if I meet it?

Answers on a postcard please.

There are more words for me during this month in Moniaive, mostly about patience, "allowing answers to unfold quietly in the dark" and "keeping interested" to keep "ever moving forward". But I am accompanied on my journey by many other sounds. One night, alone in the atmospheric sitting room, I hear the sound of beating wings flying directly over my head. Large wings. It was so loud and close that I ducked and looked around me. It didn't feel malevolent. It was definitely not the usual sound of bats I normally heard in the loft above, but there was nothing to be seen. Later, while meditating, I felt a loving pink figure with silver wings. I said to myself, "No, it can't be – it looks like an angel." However, this is what I felt I saw. Is this my loving guide? Is this the new pink energy I have been waiting for? When will more be revealed?

6

Winter approaches. My first visit to Moniaive is at an end and I leave to spend some time in Lanzarote where the energy will, I am sure, be rather different. When I look back on my experiences in Moniaive, I am struck with the thought, *Who sets the stage? And when?* I think of how and when I met Grisel and the impact she has had on my life and I often wondered why I kept on visiting her. She was a much older woman and from an aristocratic background, rather different from mine. But it seems clear that, five years earlier when I met her at The Boat of Garten Nature Cure retreat, the plot was already hatched – once more an indication of how we struggle through life and all the time the master plan is in place.

Can I manage the next stage of my life without struggle? Stop worrying about my future? Where will I be? What am I going to do? I can tell myself intellectually that there is nothing to fear, but I don't yet feel it in my bones. I need some inspiration. Wait! I remember a quote from Wendell Berry that feels very sustaining:

"It may be, when we no longer know what to do, we have come to our real work and then, when we no longer know which way to go, we have begun our real journey."

Yes, I like that and so the year starts with feelings of hopefulness. A new year, a new start and a new start of any kind prompts us to rethink. It's an opportunity to try again, to get it right. What desolation when we realize we have made a mess of something and will never have a fresh chance to try again and, conversely, what joy when we are allowed another shot at it. This is why, I think, that the concept of reincarnation is of comfort. We can look on that as a chance to get it right, which is really what evolution is all about. It's not about humans beating themselves up for getting it wrong, but the knowledge that everything evolves through certain stages before being transformed into something else. Sure, we should strive to be the best we can on our particular journeys, but not to the point of despair or despising the self. Part of the process of evolution is, I think, that we are given certain handicaps or boundaries to deal with and it is the way in which we strive to overcome or make the best of these that may give us 'good grades'. I don't believe it is about punishment, although I understand why it can be seen that way. If we look at this life as being the only one we are ever going to have then it is devastating to have too much struggle. But, if we look at this life as only one in the great scheme of things, our attitude can change. In fact, our entire philosophy of life can change. We no longer need to look at others as 'wrong' or 'evil', but perhaps as people who are also doing their best in the lessons of their evolution. We are all souls on a journey, but there is so much judgment of each other – everyone has their own code and thinks his or hers is the right one. Clichéd as it may sound, acceptance and non-judgment is the key to universal love and compassion. Lecture over….

Writing as Meditation

Natalie Goldberg, in her wonderful and inspiring book, *Writing Down the Bones*, says, "Writers do not write to impart knowledge, they write to inform themselves." She also advises using writing as meditation practice, which is a practice that I have embraced. I meditate and write my thoughts daily, learning little insights (or feeling I do), and every once in a while I am struck with the Eureka! principle. First, I read dozens of books and hundreds of theories and concepts. I can read them over and over without a deep-seated understanding or even without any understanding, until one day a little something happens and "Eureka!" I say. "Oh! That's what you meant" and a concept or theory slots perfectly into place.

Knowledge is experience. It is the same feeling as Eureka! Something happens in your life and the theory or concept is called upon and you discover whether or not it works. There is a big difference in intellectually accepting a theory and experiencing it. Once experienced, your belief becomes unshakeable as you *know* it to be true (for you). Meditation helps me to reach this point. I can *see* a concept sometimes through meditation; the loose ends fall into place and it becomes more whole. Again, I feel it to be 'experience' rather than theory. I believe that we should only stand up and speak our truth if we have this kind of experiential understanding and not put forward worn-out theories. I look forward to being able to do that sometime, but, meanwhile, keeping paper and pencil beside me as I meditate means any elusive inspirational thought, any remarkable or uplifting idea, can be anchored. What is then written on the page is pure. No censor. Unadulterated, original, creative thought.

7

Still in Lanzarote, I am taking part in a group meditation to mark the arrival of the Age of Aquarius. Spirit of White Eagle appears to me then seems to retreat and as he does so, a new pink light comes into view. Is this to do with the love I still have to learn?

That night I had a seemingly sleepless but dreaming night full of weird and wonderful pictures. I saw beautiful little winged creatures – so beautiful they made me cry. I also had the strong feeling that the healing/therapies I was trying were not helping the asthma problem I had. I felt that we were working on the wrong vibration. Something or someone from a very high vibration was needed to lift it out. There was a very definite feeling of lifting it out. Was this what the new pink light repeatedly and mysteriously hinted at?

A few days later I had a clairvoyant reading by Paul Lambillion who told me there was a new pink light just coming into my life. He was assuming that this was a new man, a new love, but I didn't think so. He told me I had something new to learn, though he didn't know what. He then told me that if I got the opportunity to go to South America I should definitely go. Sure thing, methinks!

A couple of days after that, I had a 'chance' meeting with a chap called Peter the Great, who was a stage hypnotist. We chatted about healing and the role of hypnosis and he also told me about his work with past life regression, of which I knew nothing. *Very interesting*, I thought.

Moving deeper into the year, however, April, and I am back in Moniaive. I resolve to be more disciplined with daily meditations and am depressed that my relationship has not worked out and I am on my own again. It is hard to concentrate. I feel no contact. No topics spring to mind. Is this a time for 'no mind'?

I consider the words of Alec Milne – "surrender to life" – but I don't really understand what this means. Am I fighting against things in life? I'm fighting against illness I suppose, but according to Alec's Nature Cure philosophy, I'm ill because I don't surrender. What does this mean? I can make an affirmation, but I don't really understand what I'm affirming, apart from 'Thy Will is my will', but there is no Eureka! here for me. Just have to watch this space.

The Archetype and the Ego

I was contemplating the previous incarnations that I had been told of or that I had seen for myself in meditation, such as Aborigine Shaman, Atlantean princesses, being in the temples of India and Egypt, a monk, a nun, a North American Indian tribal leader – all big guns – and wondering to myself *why* I was so lacking in self-confidence. *Why* was I still unwell and tired and not able to be out in the world shaking it all about? Then I remembered archetypes and thought, *Ah ha! I'll just go and tap into one now.*

And so, I ask for the archetype most able to help me to appear now, and coming towards me is a procession of people holding aloft a beautiful woman, dressed very splendidly in deep blue robes of luxurious material. She is wearing an ornate headdress encrusted with gold and jewels and is being carried on a sort of grand pallet, which is lowered for her to step off and walk toward me. She is amused at the shock on my face and I am shocked at the richness of her appearance.

She laughed as she says to me, "Be comfortable and enjoy! You are of no use to Spirit if you are cowering in a corner. The ego needs some arrogance to propel you forwards. The ego is necessary to survive in the world. Call on me any time you need me." Then, she and her entourage were off.

Fantastic! Strut your stuff, Carol. I thought, and decided that I must remember my archetypes more often. So, buoyed with this success, I entered a phase of calling upon help every day.

I asked for my inner healer and had an interesting experience of Jesus who appeared in the meadow under my tree, the place I hurry to in my mind. A beautiful light emanated from him and I was very shy in his presence. He told me to stand but I was so afraid to look into his face, as I was sure he would see all my impurities. He was gentle and encouraging and told me that peace was what I needed and to greet each new day with joy. Didn't expect to see him.

Next day, I hurried to my tree in the meadow and asked for an archetype to come and help me with my lack of confidence, courage and knowledge of who I am (I was having a tearful morning). A female appeared who looked like an Aztec or Incan Indian and was referred to as Ancient Wisdom. She wore a brightly-coloured beaded top and a sort of apron around her waist. She sat down opposite me and said she had always been with me, but I had never called on her before. I tearfully told her how I was feeling.

"What is my purpose? Where am I in the scheme of things?" I asked.

She told me that I should meet with her every day as these were big questions and that, as Spirit of White Eagle always told me, I should stand tall. She said that I must be open to the universe (I see myself standing, arms outstretched, face upwards) and open to abundance. "You can only share treasures and joy if you have them," she said. "If you are not open to them, you cannot share them with others. All of the archetypes are telling you similar things. You are a child of God. Be open and receive."

I promised I would meet with her every day and she left.

This was her message the following day:

"You must be tall. You must be proud. The blue-robed priestess was right; the ego needs some arrogance. You are spiritual enough to know the limits. Walk your talk. Be open to everything. Stand under the moon. Feel the elements. You are cold because you won't open to the element of cold and winter. They too are part of the scheme of things. But first, love yourself and be sure of your inner light and conviction. Be proud. You are not really projecting this confidence. I will help. See, look at me, puffing out the chest, proud of who I am, as God made me, as God wants me to be, no better or worse than any of God's creatures. I am that I am – said by God and true for us all. You are taking steps to educate yourself so you feel confident. This is good on the outward plane. Combine this with inner security and your star will truly shine."

She also reminded me not to forget pleasures of the earth – intimacy, laughter, friends. "Otherwise you wouldn't be part of the earth," she said. "Dance and sing and laugh. This helps release your energy centres. Pleasure soars through your veins and your circulation. Come back tomorrow."

We said goodbye and she put her hands on my shoulders and looked into my face, and I did likewise.

At our next meeting she told me more about openness, surrender, sending colour to my centres and strengthening the aura. I said I would try. She then sat cross-legged in front of me to tell me a tale.

"There was a young squaw who was desperate to know all the secrets. She pestered all the wise old men and pestered the medicine women who would have nothing to do with her. She eavesdropped on the wise men and one day took the pipe with the leaves to give her 'enlightenment'. But when she smoked the pipe the inside of her head blew up. Smoke and debris flew from her nose and ears. She would not appreciate all the other stuff she had to learn first. She had no patience. She did not die, but she never became a wise woman and did only menial work in the tribe."

"Wow!" I said. "Is that true?"

"No," she laughed, "but it could be!"

We said goodbye and parted, still laughing. But our encounters were leaving me with so many lessons to ponder. Firstly, a change in my ideas about ego? I had always thought that ego was a self-important, big-headed kind of thing. Perhaps that is Ego with a big E. Ego of the personality as opposed to soul ego. This is something to be investigated. Then there was joy, openness and laughter to be considered: all reminders to take part in life. Today's spiritual seekers are not the hermits of old and it is a great challenge to have one's feet on the ground while intent on soaring heavenward.

And patience, patience, patience.

8

Cutting Ties

There is an excellent book called *Cutting the Ties that Bind* by Phyllis Krystal, which shows us how to identify the people, places and things that drain us or hold us back. It is a powerful technique, which I have used for myself and for others. I have also used it to work on cutting ties with my ex-lover, as I felt grief for the loss of our relationship. It was slow and painful and I had great difficulty letting him go.

The way it worked was for me to visualize us both in an ocean, which helped as I could imagine him being separate from me but together still in the vast seascape. I cried great tears every time he left my sight, but many days of cutting ties passed and slowly it got easier. I thanked him for all the wonderful times, for all he'd taught me and for his generosity. We kissed and hugged and I felt that he would now be happier, and that helped.

It felt like a dying experience – how to let go and move on. I also realized that love and relationships always meant sadness for me in the past and I no longer wanted this pattern. I want to love freely and let go without holding on if love does not want to stay. Too much of my life has been holding on to sorrow and I now choose not to do that. I will give and receive love wherever this is possible – friends, family, my nieces; give and receive openly as if my life depended on it, or even my death! Not morbid; full of life; full of love – love, the beautiful essence of human existence.

But when this love is kept inside in a hurt place it ferments, darkens and turns poisonous. When mixed with other sour emotions it absorbs these qualities, like jealousy, fear, possessiveness. We must let love out, mix it with the ethers. If our love stagnates and rots, can we open the door in our heart and ask the Universe for a fresh supply? Is this the role of the healer? An opener of doors? What a nice thought.

At my next attempt at cutting ties there are no tears and no pain: just a lovely peaceful meditation full of beautiful swirling colours. At last. I can move on.

I See an Angel

That summer, while living in The Stables in Moniaive, I became very unwell and had to be hospitalized for a few days. Then, in my isolated convalescence, I was very sick and vomiting twenty-four hours a day. I chose to be left alone and turned down all offers to be looked after, but I was lonely, angry and yelling at 'them upstairs', demanding proof: if I had to be sick and isolated in the name of Spirit – alone, unloved and unlovely – where the hell were they?

So, exhausted, in the middle of a dark, dark night after countless visits to the toilet bowl, I fell back into bed not bothering to put out my bedside lamp, assuming I'd be back up again very shortly. I slept a little then woke up to see, at the bottom of my bed a shimmering, iridescent, moving shape, like thousands of tiny bubbles containing all of the colours of the spectrum, ever-changing and free-forming.

"Wow!" I said. "That's lovely."

It had the quality of a heat haze, transparent yet still obvious, and in my sleepy state I assumed that I must have left the centre light on and it had overheated. So I watched the dancing lights for a while, turned over and put out the bedside lamp, but then I realized the centre light had never been on and the shape at the bottom of my bed was an angel. I smiled and fell asleep with a lovely inner glow, slept till morning, no more vomiting, and slowly I started improving. Imagine that – an angel.

Shoshana, Natalie and Channelling White Buffalo Woman

The little village of Moniaive and surrounding hamlets and towns attract many artists, writers and healers. The countryside is beautiful and the lifestyle tranquil. It was this attraction that led me to meet Shoshana and Natalie; a couple of friends who were Reiki healers had met them in America and had invited them to Scotland to do some work as well as some sightseeing. These two fascinating women were channellers. Shoshana channelled Red Feather and Natalie channelled White Buffalo Woman.

I first met them at our hosts', Peter and Ro's, beautiful home, about half an hour's worth of wiggly roads away from me, for an evening of channelling, followed the next day with individual readings, to be booked in advance.

The evening was very well attended and without having met either of these women I had decided intuitively to choose Natalie for my individual session. When I saw them, however, I felt that I must have made the wrong choice. I was instantly attracted to the energy of one of the women, but she looked so exotic that I thought she must be Shoshana and I was disappointed. However, I was mistaken. She was indeed Natalie and she was the one who channelled White Buffalo Woman.

People were chosen from the audience to come forward and sit on the floor with them. Then White Buffalo Women spoke in a language that sounded very ancient and as she spoke she worked, pulling and joining invisible threads in the energy fields of the person in front of her, blowing sharply into the body through the skin. Quite fascinating. Then, Shoshana, channelling Red Feather, would translate (in English) what White Buffalo Woman had said and what advice had been given. One after another, people were called forward and time was moving on. I had not been called, but I kept telling myself that it was ok as I had an individual session booked for the next day. *Let someone else have a chance*, I thought, but then Red Feather grunted and nodded at me, so off I went.

I sat on the floor facing White Buffalo Woman and she started to speak to me. Her words, her sound, was so ancient that it seemed to speak to my bones. I was transfixed by the sound of the words. White Buffalo Woman did some pulling and blowing and tapping then looked to Red Feather to translate and *he* said, "I don't need to translate. This one knows all you are saying." Then she looked at me and said, "Don't you."

It was hard to answer. My bones seemed to know, but my mind did not. I think maybe I nodded dumbly.

White Buffalo Woman thinks we are finished but Red Feather says, "No. Michael needs to speak to her. He needs to speak now."

Unusual. Mutterings from the room. No-one else had Michael! (And, by the way, we are talking Archangel Michael here, not just any Michael.)

So, after a slight adjustment of energy, Natalie's voice brings through Michael. Now I am completely blown away as *the* most beautiful *pink* energy descends and envelops me and I am in bliss with the feelings of love. Natalie (Michael) says strongly to me, "Thou must believe in thee. Thou must *Believe* in thee. We have tried to tell you, but you would not listen. Now God himself has come forward and said 'Thou Must Believe in Thee'."

I don't remember much more, just that I felt in love and I

couldn't speak to anyone. I left quickly, drove the wiggly roads home then I slept happily but woke late. I had my pre-booked session with Natalie and I had to rush, except I could barely function. I felt beaten up and nauseous as if I had had a wild and drunken night. How would I make it back up those roads? But, I got there, looking and feeling completely wrecked. Did I have flu?

"Oh, I feel so bad," I said to Natalie.

She laughed and said, "That's good," and carried on with her healing, unbinding my shoulders and hips, all the while transporting me with her ancient tribal words. Michael came through again and I got more of a ticking off about 'coming forward, believing in myself and loving myself'. He was the new pink energy in my life, an energy so full of sustaining comfort and love. Unforgettable. I was completely wrapped in love and more than ready to come forward into the next adventure.

9

Past Life Healing

Footloose and fancy-free, wondering what's next, my eyes and ears are open for welcoming signs.

One day, while house-sitting for my brother, I was flicking through a little notebook, looking for something or other, and there I saw 'College of Past Life Healing' together with 'Diane Park' and a telephone number. It was my writing. When did I do that?

Intrigued, I phoned the number and spoke to Diane Park and – hurrah! – there were bells in my head and butterflies in my tummy. She described the training course, their way of working and philosophy, and everything was just as I would have chosen. No doubts. I signed myself up and soon was off to Wales. Three trains, two buses and a car ride and I was on the banks of the River Tyvie about to embark on a ten-day adventure into other realms.

Diane's house, where the course was being held, was at the bottom of a very steep hill close to the river. This was slate country and the house and garden had been built in what had been a quarry. On two sides were steep, constantly dripping walls of dark slate. High walls and rampant vegetation sealed in the other sides. Womb-like. It was, on many levels, another world. Inside the house, old beams sighed and puffed dust. Sunlight was a bit of a stranger, but there was a big open fire for telling stories round and a huge help-yourself-and-tidy-up-afterwards kitchen.

The philosophy in brief is healing the emotional body in this life and in all other lives, and once my fellow travellers (all *simpatico* women) and Diane's partner Beccy arrived, we were off! But I soon discovered that this training was not for casual tourists. It was hard and completely engrossing work. We started straight after breakfast, sometimes lunch was very late afternoon or sometimes not at all. Same with dinner, although we did eat well when there was time, and we worked till late at night. We had completely left the world outside the garden walls and had no concept of time or place. Only fascination. I learned so much. Diane was an excellent teacher as she was a very experienced therapist and an extremely committed person.

There were days of tears, anger, rage, grief and squabbling amongst ourselves as we were encouraged to let go! Let go! Let go! Let go of the stuffed-down emotions. But, wonderful personal stories emerged, which served not only to feed our fascination, but also to effect profound healing.

In the first few days we were learning the induction – the bit where we talk the client into a state of deep relaxation – and we paired off to practise, one being client and one being therapist. I was client, lying comfortably, expecting nothing from this dress rehearsal.

My therapist started the script but as far as I was concerned, she immediately faded out as a picture emerged in my mind of a young woman, walking the ramparts of a fortified town. I could even feel the wind tugging at my (*my?*) long pointed hat, which had only a chiffon ribbon to hold it around my neck. Yes, I was identifying with this young woman. I was on the outside looking in, but I was also the one on the inside. I felt immense sadness as she looked out towards the horizon.

My therapist's voice was stronger, urging me to "walk slowly down the stairs" and I (*she*) reacted with, "No! I'm not going down there."

I (*me on the outer*) could sense the bewilderment of my therapist as she tried again to persuade me down the stairs.

"No!" (*she*) stubbornly refused. I then sensed my therapist waving over to Diane for help and together they tried to create a more friendly descent but I (*she*) finally said, "No. Can't you smell them? The dungeons. I'm not going there again."

Ah ha! Diane understood that I wasn't being belligerent, but had slipped into a past life and there was nothing else for it but to let it unfold. I sensed everyone gathering around for the live show as Diane took me back to the start of my story.

There it is. The house of my childhood. As I remembered it before the Black Day. The day my life was given away. The house nestled between gentle green hills, as if over the years it had rooted itself, nudging the trees and hills to its liking. Memories of laughter, of running and tumbling and giggling with my sisters. Always a tumbling and jumbling giggle of girls. Was there laughter still? Was it easy to forget me, my sisters, my mother? And my father? How did he reconcile his heart? I was in the kitchen helping my mother the day he rode up to the house, grim-faced and silent, snatching me from my household duties, throwing me onto his horse and galloping off across the hills. No words spoken. No time for goodbyes. No explanations.

I had never been out of sight of the house before, so a journey such as this should have been interesting, but I was afraid, afraid of the speed and the silence and the sense of something terrible taking place. As we approached the fortified town and the castle I knew that 'terrible' did not have a deep enough meaning.

The great hall of the castle was vast and so cold. Huge fireplaces with blazing fires did little to remove the chill. Or was the chill only in my heart? A serving woman appeared, nodded to my father and took me roughly by the hand, leading me along dark hallways. She was grim-faced and silent too. Her hand gripped mine and I had to run to keep up with her. Huge tapestries hung at the end of the hallway draping either side of a large studded door. The serving woman opened the door and we entered. A vast bed dominated the room: high and wooden with tapestries all the way round. That is all I remember seeing – the huge bed.

The serving woman said, 'Sit,' and 'Wait,' and she was gone.

So I sat on the great bed and I waited, too frozen with dread to move or think. The door burst open and so it felt did my heart, as my eyes saw for the first time that malevolence of a man, that black-souled abomination, who threw my skirts over my head and raped me. When he was done I heard him shout, as he thundered away down the hallway, "Tell the father she will do. Give him his bit of land." It seems I had been sold for an extra bit of pasture.

The same serving woman came back for me, more gentle now, bundled me up and took me to a smaller and warmer room where she bathed me. Strange, I had felt almost nothing at all. I didn't feel quite present and it seemed that I had watched the whole gory scene from somewhere above the bed, way up in the corner.

As the years went on he had other distractions, but he demanded me often. I had no choice but to present myself at the big bed. When I did refuse I was beaten, but much worse than that was the dungeon. Down deep under the castle where even the rats eyes were blinded, with no light and the smell of damp and fear that turned the strongest of stomachs. There, the instruments of torture lay in wait like hungry monsters. Screams and groans were commonplace and I became immune, dreading much more the black silence, as I lived through each punishment, chained hand and foot to the slimy wall, hatred my only companion. Perhaps I shouldn't have clawed his face or spat on him, but I could not help it. I hissed and spat and clawed at the very thought of his presence.

I hated everyone in that godforsaken place. My only pleasure was the dressmaker and the fine clothes. I loved the pretty materials and I remember the silver and lilac brocades made into dresses and shoes for me. My tall pointed hats had matching chiffon to tie under my chin. I often walked the battlements where the wind would whip my hat and I would feel wobbly and need to slide along the walls, but up there I could see for miles. I could see sky and hills and I could imagine another life in another place.

Tonight, I thought, I will be better behaved. I will hold my tongue. In the great hall at the long table, his soldiers and women of distraction were eating and drinking and he, as loud and fat and disgusting as ever, presided over them all. Sitting there, I lifted my eyes to see gentle blue eyes observing me. A flash of bright blue crackled between us and pain so sharp I thought I had been shot through with an arrow, pierced just below my ribs. I gasped. I couldn't help it. I couldn't quite get a proper breath. Good lord, he was beautiful! Soft curls the colour of corn just before harvest. Smooth skin, smooth neck, gentle mouth. I had an overwhelming desire to taste that gentle mouth and my eyes returned to his lips and eyes again and again. The world around me ceased to exist for a few wild heartbeats. Oh, my love. The love of all my lives. Simon was his name and we plotted and schemed just to see each other, brush past each other, whisper a word of longing. We both knew a terrible death would be ours if we were discovered, but somehow we planned an escape. He was a soldier and he had a horse. There was a way out, through the garden, beyond the maze. We would meet there and we would escape and we would at last hold each other. The longing was breaking my heart. I was willing to risk all and so it was planned.

But no! Something was wrong. I had such a foreboding. I knew. I knew something, Simon! Had our plan been discovered? I went to the garden and ran through the maze in blind panic. No Simon. No one. Had he been captured?

The dungeon. My God he's in the dungeon. The malevolent one had a gallery where he could view his victims being tortured below in the dungeons and that is where I ran to. And there was my love. Impaled on giant metal teeth, his beautiful body run through, already dead. Oh, I could not live without him. I climbed onto the rail of the gallery and threw myself down onto the same spikes that held my love and I can tell you, there was no pain. Only bliss. Simon and I were united in a blissful embrace.

Together at last, making our final journey together – in that lifetime.

End of story. Still in bliss, I am aware of a few sobs and sighs from the other women, affected by my story. Diane starts the healing part of the process and I let go of so many emotions that no longer serve me. The mental and physical bodies are healed but the big vows and statements made by me (her) needed attention and had to be cleared out of my life. These were three of the big ones:

Love is always out of reach
You can only love in Spirit
I'll never love like that again

Afterwards, I felt clear, able to breathe, still very touched by the beauty and immensity of that love, but I also knew I could now move on with love in this life.

This work is not for the faint-hearted, but I survived it, loved it and joined up for the second part of the training later in the year.

After ten days of other-wordliness it was noisy and busy outdoors, but I made the two buses and three trains' journey home feeling lighter and smilier and looking forward to a summer of letting go.

What a Summer

Back in Moniaive to my isolation, I was enjoying my feelings of lightness and being unburdened and for a while everything was going well, until something released tears. I let them happen. All part of the training. I cried all day, all evening and woke up crying the next morning. I did the housework, hung out the washing, crying. Day followed day of crying hot fat tears. I had turned into a weather report – loud squalls followed by prolonged drizzle. I could have irrigated a small African village! Eventually I stopped noticing and the tears spurted silently. I realized I was crying for my mother, my father, my son and my lover. I had tapped into grief and it was huge, so huge it had moved in and opened an office. I must have tapped into universal grief as it went on and on. Living in splendid isolation, I did nothing to stop the tears, although it is debatable that they could have been stopped. The paradox was I didn't feel depressed or suicidal, just aware of grief splashing down my face. And then one day it stopped and that was that. Took a big breath. Next…

Yelling at Jesus

I am not a Jesus follower any more than I am Buddha or Archangel or Master follower. I respect all, can feel love and appreciation for their philosophies, etc. but I don't really join up, if you know what I mean. So it was a surprise to me when it was Jesus who appeared to me in my meditation during this time of emotional release.

As I sit in meditation, I am transported to an isolated shore and Jesus arrives in a little boat. He is so beautiful and I am very happy and humble to see him. He sits beside me and takes my hand and I want to say, "Jesus, please help me. Please tell me why I'm feeling so unwell." But, when I open my mouth to say this to the beautiful earnest face of Jesus, out comes the scream of a harridan. "Jesus, what the f*@k is going on?" I commence shouting, screaming, growling and stamping up and down in the physical as well as in the meditational! In the physical, I get up and put my wellies on and shout and stamp around the garden, frightening the sheep with all the bad language until eventually I calm down, go back indoors, feeling a great sense of release. I later prepare to go about my day when, suddenly, I remember about poor Jesus. Oh my God, I swore at Jesus and I had just left him there! So, I hurry back to my meditational space. He looks very shaky – I had blasted him from such close quarters and with such ferocity that his hair has been blown straight back like a scene from a cartoon.

"Oh, Jesus, I'm so sorry," I said.

"It's all right," he replied as he tried to look composed and unhurried, but he, nonetheless, scarpered quickly and rowed away on his boat. It became a bit of a joke between us after that.

The weekly meditation/healing meetings in The Stables sustained me, bringing warmth and empathy into my life as well as human company. In fact, I think I started babbling like a maniac when I had visitors due to the underuse of social interaction. I had even started talking to the mice who marched in behind the skirting boards late in the evening.

"Evening chaps," I shouted.

I released my repertoire of jokes onto the spiders (or speeders as they are called here due to their size and velocity), getting annoyed if they didn't hang around for the punchline. Then, I threatened them with the hoover.

Following on from the episode of continual tears, I had entered a phase of also telling jokes to myself. I laughed and laughed. The good thing about telling jokes to yourself is that you can go straight to the punchline! One day, after one really good belly laugh, I stopped short and said to myself, "My God, that's it. I've gone mad. Fantastic!" And I laughed even more. *If this is madness,* I thought, *bring it on.*

There were other sustaining things, like opening the door to the sitting room and suddenly finding it full of butterflies (and once full of sheep eating the flowers in the vase) or the emergence of a pheasant with nine or ten of her babies from under a bush in the garden and the shy family of deer who came out to play in the gloaming. The hills I looked out upon, constantly changed colour, the mists swirled and shadows appeared and disappeared in a flash. I thought I would get on with so many creative things while I was here, but all I seemed to do was look out of the window and watch the ever-changing hills, mesmerized.

There was also a party or two with fantastic music from local musicians and amnesia producing local hooch. People went missing for days after a good party.

10

And so ended another chapter. As winter approached I left Moniaive, did the second part of my Past Life Healing training and wandered about some more searching for the 'next' in my life. This is what I found:

In a magazine, I read an article about John of God, a healer in Brazil, and remembered the words of Paul Lambillion, the Clairvoyant who told me that if I get the opportunity to go to South America I should definitely go. The bells! The bells in my head! Loud and strong! Here is where I must go!

I contacted Caterina and Robert, an Australian couple who took groups of people from all over the world to meet Joao Teixeira de Faria, also known as John of God, the Miracle Man. Caterina and Robert smoothed the journey and supported those who underwent healing. I thought I would go there and perhaps, through observation, could improve on my healing skills. Maybe I'd find a whole new path.

I was very excited and spent many weeks organizing the trip, the flights, hotels and learning some basic Portuguese until it was time to set off. I had also spent quite a bit of time communing with the spirits and entities that Joao worked with. I forewarned them of my visit, asking to receive all that I needed to receive and felt comfortable and open about all that might befall me. But before the first leg of my journey was over, strange things had already started happening.

Sitting on the plane, I noticed my left forearm was very itchy and when I eventually looked I saw I had a large red weal. The itch moved and more large weals appeared, hot and itchy. By the time I reached Rio de Janeiro I wished I had packed calamine lotion as my limbs and my torso were on fire. I was too excited to be troubled by this, but by the following evening I looked like a burns victim and my feet were fiery red and so swollen that they hung over the sides of my shoes. Caterina, however, just smiled and said, "Nothing to worry about." And I knew she was right; everything was as it should be. Somehow, I felt that I was being cleansed and prepared for what was ahead.

My hotel room looked directly on to Ipanema Beach and it was hard to leave the view and sleep. Day and night there was activity on the beautiful white sandy beach because people live right there. Fabulous Latin jazz was being played by impromptu musicians and everyone dances there, even people with limbs missing. I saw a woman with no feet who had to walk on all fours, stop and dance to the music. There were many disabled people and very few wheelchairs. Grown people got around in prams and one chap with no legs zipped along on a skateboard. I was amazed to see on the beach one day, a young and curvaceous woman, wearing a Tonga bikini. Why amazing? She was no taller than a two-year-old child and was sitting in a kiddie car. No one was hidden away. The poor lived on the streets (one couple I saw with twin toddlers lived on a tablecloth on the pavement) and the wealthy have armed guards and dogs to protect their apartment buildings and bodyguards when they go out. Absolutely fascinating, but I had to leave to head for the semi-remote region of Goais and the village of Abadiania to fulfil the purpose of my visit.

First, we flew to Brasilia then took a three-hour bus journey into the heart of Brazil. A tremendous lightning storm heralded our arrival in this small 'one-horse town' and great plops of rain crashed down on the tin roof of the place we were to stay in for the next few days. It was a very basic *pousada* or pensione. I had paid extra for single accommodation and so I had the luxury of a toilet next to my room, away from the main building and the noise. My room, which was more like a semi-detached hut, had a single bed, a light bulb swinging from a cord and a window with metal shutters, but no glass. The roof was corrugated tin with a huge gap around the top of the walls through which flashes of lightning lit up my room and the electricity had blown with the storm. Fortunately for me, I love the sound of rain on tin roofs and I love lightning storms, so I was happy and comfortable.

I was not the only excited one. No one could sleep and there seemed to be noise of happy chattering and showering and coffee-making all night long. The day started early and what a day it was.

At 7.30 a.m. we set off to walk to the healing sanctuary and already the sun was drying the remains of the storm from the red earth. The sky was clear blue and ahead the mist was rising like a mystical carpet from the valley. A perfect day for miracles. Hundreds and hundreds of people dressed in pilgrim white arrived on foot, in cars and on buses to meet the healer/medium at his sanctuary called La Casa de Dom Inacio.

It is there that Joao is taken over by Entity (Dom Inacio, otherwise known as St Ignatius, is one of his main Entities) and performs the most amazing spirit operations. These operations are carried out both visibly and invisibly. He has been studied and scrutinized, beaten, persecuted and imprisoned, but this amazing man continues to heal thousands of people every week – presidents of countries, film stars, poor illiterate peasants. People come from all over the world, but Joao accepts no money or recompense.

The group of people I am with includes many very sick people, many of whom have already been given terminal diagnoses by their doctors. Some have been told they only have weeks to live. For them, the first miracle is that they managed to get there. Friendships are forged fast and the love and support given to one another is truly beautiful.

Meanwhile, I seemed to have turned into a crybaby. In the main hall of the sanctuary there are mothers with their sick babies, fathers carrying disabled children, stretchers bearing loved ones, everyone praying for a miracle. The atmosphere is so highly charged with emotion and with hope and my heart is so overwhelmed by it all that I just can't stop the fat, hot, useless tears.

When it is time to meet Joao and be 'scanned' by Entity, we queue and file slowly through the first room. This has about thirty or forty mediums sitting in meditation or 'in current' as they call it here. The purpose of the current is to send energy to the Entities so that they can be present to work with Joao, and also to spiritually cleanse everyone who passes through on their way to meet Joao. The current could also be called psychic energy or healing energy or even focused good thoughts.

In a corner there is a mound of discarded wheelchairs, crutches and body braces. A second room has even more mediums and also people who have been told to sit there to be cleansed or healed by the current. Joao sits in a huge wicker chair and greets each one. The energy that surrounds him is immense and I am dumbstruck. His hand is outstretched to take mine and I hear him say that I have to have an operation. Today? Who me? I'm there to witness and experience sitting with the mediums and I imagined any healing would take place while sitting quietly doing this. An operation? I am intrigued.

Over lunch we chatter and swap stories and I notice I feel extra relaxed and a bit spacey. I then start to smell a very sweet smell and ask those near me, "Do you smell that?" All shake their heads and say, "No." More and more sleepy I feel and sweeter the smell.

We have returned to the sanctuary for the afternoon's

operations when suddenly I am doubled over with a pain in my lower abdomen. Caterina sees this and I am whipped off to the recovery room to rest.

"Entity is working on you now," she says. "Just lie quietly and you will be healed."

A few of our group are also there, strange things having befallen them. One woman was, she said, "lifted off my feet and thrown against a wall". She had bumped her head, later revealing that she had an undiagnosed, small brain tumour, which Entity was healing. If she had not had the bump on the head she would not have co-operated.

Most of the operations are done en masse and invisibly, but some are done in the main hall in front of everyone and recorded on video. Joao does this to ensure that everyone can see and therefore believe that he works hand in hand with the Divine. No tricks.

At this point I think that I have had my invisible operation, but no. I am ushered towards the hall and at the last minute I hear myself volunteer for a visible operation and allow myself to be led, along with five others, onto the platform in the hall. I am last in line and the sweet smell I now realize is spiritual anaesthetic. I am told to keep my eyes closed, but I can't help peeking – I see a man having huge abscesses removed from his head then a woman having an incision in her abdomen. Another woman has cataracts removed from her eyes and Joao is using what looks like a tomato knife! I see trays of gleaming surgical instruments and a man with a mop to clean up blood, and I see hundreds and hundreds of pairs of eyes. Oh God, what am I doing here?

I am moved onto the middle of the platform. Strong hands hold me by the shoulders and then they grab and squeeze my breasts and my abdomen. My breath is taken away by the violence and I want to protest when suddenly the inside of my head explodes and I literally see red. I hear the sound of grinding bones as my septum is moved out of the way and I hear loud rushing noises. I am appalled but somehow comprehend that Joao is using surgical scissors to operate and is entering my body via my nose. But why? Soon it's over and I am taken in a chair to the recovery room, warm blood trickling down my face.

Later, I return to my bijou residence where I lie quietly, feeling very nauseous. Just as in the 'real world' the anaesthetic makes me feel sick. I also have a very sore nose, a shocking headache and an ache in my abdomen. Everyone is very kind, bringing me lovely drinks of freshly pressed mango or papaya or a morsel to eat and Caterina checks up on me, but will not be drawn into conversation about what had happened to me.

"Just lie still. You have had major surgery. Rest."

And so I did. The sweet smell was still strong and I suppose kept me woozy and resting.

My neighbour was a man called John from Seattle. He had also had an operation, although an invisible one, and, like me, felt just as if he had been operated on in the 'real world'. We looked in on each other during the next day and he told me a little of his story. He had a galloping illness called Amyotrophic Lateral Sclerosis (also known as Lou Gehrig's disease) and now could hardly walk and his speech was very slurred. His great sorrow was the thought of not being around for his small son. There were so many stories in our little group of seekers, all with different reasons for being there, but all full of hope.

At last, Caterina would talk. She told me that as soon as she saw me she knew that I either had cancer or it was just starting. She saw it in my aura. Caterina was very psychic and used to work with Joao doing spirit operations. She said, "I can't believe you didn't know you were unwell."

How would I know? I thought, I never feel very well and, ok, I had lost weight, but I was always skinny.

She continued, "You have had major surgery. Entity now

says that I may tell you that you had cancer. You had a tumour on your ovary and a smaller one in your breast. Entity has removed these and you are cured."

Wow! What could I say, except "Thank you"? So, I lay still with a cold cloth over my face contemplating my experience.

After that, I didn't have the opportunity of witnessing much of, nor sitting in, the current, but fortunately I had already booked to come back to Abadiania with the next group of people being led by Caterina and Robert, and so returned to Brasilia for a few days to await them.

Two or three of the others were doing the same and so we had time to become friends and support one another during this strange convalescence. There were prescribed herbs to take and after some days we had to take part in a ritual, in our own rooms, to allow Entity to remove any 'spirit stitches' that there may be. When I lay on my bed asking for this to take place, my body started moving and vibrating and I felt finger-like movements inside my abdomen and then a dragging feeling, like stitches being pulled in my breast.

"Is that you?" I asked Entity and was answered by a tickle in my nose, which really made me laugh. "Ok," I said. "Carry on."

The next group arrived and we headed back to Abadiania. In this group there were one or two Americans and Brits, but the majority were from Slovenia and their stories were mainly about the fallout from Chernobyl and how they still had a heritage of birth defects from that disaster. Here in Brazil were some of the new generation seeking healing.

I had the opportunity of witnessing operations and sitting in current with the mediums and it was all fascinating. We were staying in a different *pousada* this time and, boy, was it luxurious. My room had glass in the window and a metal coat rack and a shelf to hang my things. This was living! Not everyone was quite so lucky and I felt a little guilty, but not guilty enough to share my solitude. I needed to sleep a lot, which I did. The food was limited in choice, but very enjoyable and the fruit was wonderful. At no time did I have any upset in the tummy department and given the primitive conditions and the quantity of ants, this was surprising. Nor did I have any mosquito bites or any other insect bites – also surprising. I felt protected during my entire trip.

Two of the group decided to stay on in the village, hoping for more healing, but for the rest of us it was back to Brasilia then to Rio where I spent a few days on my own enjoying the start of the carnival before I left. I met some interesting characters who took me to the gay parade and it was great fun. I had to resist their entreaties to teach me to samba as I had been given strict instructions – no sex, no dancing, no pork, no eggs and no alcohol for two months. My only disappointment with Brazil was the coffee. I had imagined I would sit at a beachside café indulging my love of a good coffee while watching the beautiful people of Ipanema or Copacabana. But, no, that is not the custom here. Instead they have kiosks that sell green coconuts bashed with a hatchet and a straw inserted for drinking. I tried this early one morning while out strutting my stuff along the promenade. Luckily, I was not far from my hotel as this bitter liquid is a kidney stimulant and for the rest of the piddling day I could not leave my room.

Home in Scotland, how could I explain all that had happened to me? Some experiences are just too big. I had a video of the operations at the Casa de Dom Inacio but it was a bit gruesome to watch and I had no volunteers to watch more than a few minutes. I had declared the experience life changing and, yet, it all seemed quite natural while it was occurring. The people I met were memorable. Witnessing Joao was humbling and awe-inspiring and the connection I felt with Spirit was confirmation of existence beyond the norm and that faith is worthwhile hanging onto.

*   *   *

I still had some convalescing to do and so I went with my friend Obba to Israel to visit her daughter. Obba had been having a stressful time and was very tired and we slept soundly in each other's company, which was just as well as we had to share a double bed in a little room next to a fairly large iguana.

11

Morning Light

I read a lecture given by Anne Baring, a Jungian analyst who has an excellent web page where her lectures are available to read. In this specific lecture she likens the travails of life to the transformation process of the alchemist, the alchemist's job being to turn base metal into gold. She also talks about the helpless despair of depression, which can occur through the process of transformation.

She writes, "The melancholia and suffering of the alchemist is reflected in the anguish of the life force undergoing travail and the pain of being transformed. The alchemist suffers the process of transformation. The life force in him suffers, dies, rises again."

Suffers, dies and rises again. I know these feelings. This is inspirational. As I read it I felt a sense of purpose as opposed to failure. Purpose gives me a reason to continue. Hey, one day I may be made of the stuff of gold.

So, continue I do. I read an advertisement. A healing sanctuary/therapy centre was looking for a therapist to work with them in a voluntary capacity and in return it offered accommodation, food and the opportunity to gain experience. As I am homeless, rootless and desperate to do some work this seems heaven-sent.

The centre is called Morning Light and it is on the banks of Loch Tummel in Perthshire – an added bonus to be in such beautiful countryside. Really, I could not ask for more, so I applied, explained my credentials and my physical limitations and we agreed that I would work when I felt well and rest when I did not.

Clive and Peggy, a very caring and charitable couple, owned the centre. As well as coming for a holiday, guests could receive healing every day in the sanctuary if they wished, as well as therapy offered by Clive for those in need – therapy plus a lot of support. I helped with some follow-up support to Clive's work, as did other volunteers. I also gave healing in the sanctuary, which was healing for me too, and I practised past life healing.

It was a bit of an initiation by fire, but the past life healing technique worked really well and although I still got stage fright before a session, I loved the excitement of the unknown and having to fly by the seat of my pants, leading the client wherever the path seemed to want to take us. I would say to them that the journey was theirs, but I had a map. Phenomenal stories would unfold of love and adventure. We would tap into stories of great joy and heartrending sorrow.

The client is totally present during this process, feeling the emotions, smelling the smells and hearing the sounds. This is not a 'psychic reading', not someone else divining what you were or were not in the past. This is a reliving experience that leaves the client in no doubt (and with a memory that stays with them always) of what their past had been. The process is gentle and easy and after we look at the life we heal what needs to be healed in order for them to move on in this lifetime. This is the reason for delving into the past: to release and heal stuffed-down emotions that may have been with us lifetime after lifetime and are now so huge that they block our progress.

We are also able to heal physical wounds, which are commonly found in past lives because there were not too many career opportunities that were without danger of injury. Farmers or soldiers were very common, so lots of spear wounds and sword wounds. Horrible deaths of thirst and hunger have also left indelible stains on our blueprints and the technique that I had been taught helps to clean the slate, as it were, and have a fresh start.

My time at Morning Light was definitely challenging and a lot of the stories I heard during the follow-up support of Clive's work were difficult for me to listen to. In fact, I began to think I was not cut out for this, but when I encountered a particularly distressing story and felt overwhelmed, I put on my wellies and splashed in the Loch, walked through the woods and yelled! One such difficult story I listened to caused a reaction in me that was totally frowned upon in a therapist. In fact, a huge no-no.

A lady who had been a guest for a few days came to see me. My impression of her was that she was an attractive, well groomed, not-a-hair-out-of-place type, but very buttoned up and brittle.

I made us a cup of tea, allowing time to chat and perhaps relax her into telling her story. But her story was difficult to listen to even though she was telling it by rote like a record that had been played over and over, impersonal and detached. The problem was that my emotional buttons were being pushed, as parts of her story resonated uncomfortably with me.

"The thing is," she confessed, "I can't cry. I've tried but I just can't do it." She shrugged and looked so woebegone. "I'm sure I'd feel better," she sighed.

We talked some more and I was really struggling, holding back tears, a huge ache in my heart. Then she said a little 'matter of fact' something, I can't recall what, and the welling of suppressed tears exploded in my eyes, nose and choking throat, the lot. I just remember saying, "My son too."

"Oh!" she said and promptly burst into tears herself and once they started – Phewee! We held each other's hands;

we patted arms; we hugged and we wept until we were done.

I was embarrassed, but she had broken through her self-inflicted prison. Her eyes were red, her face puffy, but she had shed her heaviness. Her gratitude was humbling. I felt she could now start healing.

When she left me, on went the wellies and I stamped at the Loch's edge, shouting, "This is too hard. I can't do this," beating myself up for permitting this therapist's sin.

However, as I observed this lady laugh and chat with the other guests over the next few days and sing enthusiastically at our music evening, I let go of my ego. If I believed that healing comes from a higher source than me then I must accept and marvel at its ways. A little embarrassment in the scheme of things is unimportant and irrelevant.

I learned such a lot there that summer. Unfortunately, Morning Light at Loch Tummel closed its doors at the end of that summer with plans to move further north. Clive asked me to go with them, but somehow I felt compelled to return to Glasgow where I had the following dream:

A Dream of Joy

As I dropped off to sleep I felt/heard a popping noise somewhere in my head. Then I felt I was asleep as a dream started and a lovely old woman, full of laughter, who seemed to be floating on cushions, appeared to me and made me laugh. I thought how wonderfully outrageous she was. Then, a beautiful pair of shoes floated towards me and I took hold of one and admired it (the top part was made of black lace) and I thought how impractical, but fun. I wondered if I had to wear them. I felt I was awake but still 'seeing' my dream and was very aware of being told to have fun. To my left there was a water key, which had obviously been used to cut off the supply. I realized I was being told that I had cut off my own supply of joy and it was up to me to turn it back on. The theme tune from *Friends*, the television show, played over and over and over in my head: 'I'll be there for you'.

I started saying out loud, "I am willing to change. I now let joy into my life," and other such things. I was awake to hear this.

The same pictures and messages went on and on, even when I got out of bed to go to the loo. They were filled with the feeling of fun and laughter. I also felt that I had not fully appreciated being given another chance (viz. the operation and removal of cancer in Brazil). I saw at that point that I had been given a visible operation so that I could come to this understanding. I hadn't felt truly grateful.

I woke in the morning feeling hopeful and joyful although, unfortunately, completely exhausted.

(Much later on, a year or so maybe, when I had been learning about astral travel, I realized that this probably had been an astral journey. The popping sound is indicative of leaving the body, as is the corresponding exhaustion the next day!)

I had by now got used to wandering about with only the contents of a suitcase, or sometimes whatever would fit in my car, and I was very happy with just these few possessions. I did not miss my furniture and belongings that were stored in various locations about the country, but what I did feel was scattered. I felt that I had to gather everything together before being able to have a clear-out. All my things were from the past and I wanted a fresh start. That was the plan anyway. I bought a house, which ironically was in the area where I grew up. This was not by design. I just happened to be driving past and the house winked at me. It had a 'For Sale' sign and I found myself phoning an estate agent who said, "Sorry, it has just been sold."

I thought it a little strange as I had, for sure, been winked at. However, the following week the estate agent called to say that the potential buyer had a mortgage problem and the house was on the market again. So, I went to view the house and as soon as I opened the door I knew I would buy it. It was very old-fashioned and had not been decorated in a long, long time, but it felt safe and strong, which was just what I needed.

My goods and chattels started to arrive and I was horrified. Who owns all this stuff? I felt burdened, suffocated, short of breath. I did not want these things. I decided I would have to unpack and make sense of what was there before I could downsize, but slowly, as I opened boxes and greeted old friends and stacked my books on the shelves I felt a certain comfort.

The reason for writing this book was prompted by the same scattered feeling. I wanted to bring together all my notebooks, thoughts, anguish, etc. into one space.

One day after spitting onto paper my latest little drama, I happened to notice that I had used the same words in a previous entry in my notebook. I checked further back and discovered that for years I had been writing the same anguished vituperative junk.

I yelled at myself, "Good grief, woman, have you learned nothing?" The thing was, I had learned. I had learned lots then obviously forgotten it. I had not really integrated it or perhaps (to give myself the benefit of doubt) I'd moved up the spiral of learning a little, but had not yet reached wholeness. I was still going round and round. Ho hum!

But, if I had not kept my ever-filling notebooks I would not have had that realization or the tools to help me see the bigger picture. Nothing is ever wasted and I continued to write. I got into a rhythm of starting the day with some gentle yoga exercises, meditation and then writing. I wrote pages of whatever came off my pen. This could be what I'd dreamt of the night before; it could be fed-upness or anger or some feeling of insight I'd received from the meditation. But, write I did. I felt cleansed and liberated and able to see a day unfolding that would not be tainted by leftover negativity. It could be pages of bad language or temper, but that was ok. There was no censor or editor other than my own, the most critical of all, and I did not allow my critic to interfere while writing. Natalie Goldberg, in *Writing down the Bones*, writes, "If you are not afraid of the voices inside yourself, you will not fear the critics outside yourself."

When I reached this place of honest outpouring, I discovered lots of things about myself I had never before realized and fascinating stuff unfolded. Not all pretty to be sure.

I wrote myself out of chaos, to clarify my thoughts, make sense of my life, this world, humanity, Spirit. I wrote to make myself well and whole and integrated and at peace. Writing kept me in touch with myself. I could admit my imperfections to myself.

Otherwise, what do you do if you are in pain, stuck at home, lonely but proud and full of grief?

Do you yell? Don't have the energy.

Cry? Only makes you splutter and cough.

Smash the ornaments? Whoa!

Or

Write, write, write. Let it out onto paper. Then the paper can be shredded, burnt, flushed down the loo, whatever. It's out of you! It has left space for fresh air.

It was so liberating as I wrote to find that useless was not me.

Natalie Goldberg calls this outpouring 'First thoughts' and says, "You must be a great warrior when you contact first thoughts and write them. Don't stop at the tears, go straight through to truth." Fabulous stuff!

Back in the city I re-established contacts, rejoined groups

and slowly clients started to filter through. I read and studied lots about past lives, soul retrieval, spirit rescue and re-birthing, amongst other things, and used the knowledge to work quietly from a distance.

Good for the ego, I was told.

12

Among our group in Brazil was a man called Gene Keiffer with whom I had long fascinating chats. He told me about some of the coincidences and events in his life that led him onto a spiritual path. He became quite an expert on Kundalini and spent a lot of time in India with Gopi Krishna whose book, *Living with Kundalini*, was one of the first accessible books in the West on this subject. When Gopi had his Kundalini experiences he did not know who to turn to for advice and thought he was going quite mad. That was in India where there are gurus aplenty, so imagine how difficult it would have been to get information in the West. Gene had a Kundalini experience and as a result of his investigations he started the Kundalini Foundation in New York and produced many leaflets and newsletters giving easy-to-understand information. He also wrote an article called 'UFOs and Kundalini' in the book *Kundalini, Evolution and Enlightenment*, edited by John White, which I was surprised to see I had on my bookshelf and had not yet read. In the past this subject has been hidden away among the gurus and holy men, considered too dangerous for the masses. Now there are many books on the subject.

The Kundalini is referred to as 'The Fire' or 'The Coiled Serpent', which lies dormant in the base of the spine and should be left sleeping unless under the strictest of instruction from a master or guru. An awakened Kundalini is considered the way to enlightenment, but if it rises too soon it can cause madness, they say. If it rushes upwards too quickly it can destroy the energy centres. All in all, not something to be tinkered with.

Gene sent me Gopi's book to read because I had told him of some of my experiences, which felt like spontaneous Kundalini or SKs, as he refers to them. He also sent me copious amounts of his leaflets and newsletters, which usefully prepared me for what lay ahead.

The SKs I had so far experienced were small and pleasurable. They usually occurred in the early hours of the morning while still asleep. The first time I felt a sudden whoosh of energy, like a sexual surge rushing up inside me; it was so powerful I leapt out of bed and stood looking suspiciously at where I had been lying asleep, thinking "What the heck was that?" I felt slightly guilty, as if I had been having an erotic dream, which I hadn't, and I didn't mention it to anyone. The same thing happened two or three times more then stopped for maybe a few weeks before returning, sometimes very mild, sometimes stronger. This pattern continued till one surprising day.

It had been a strange day. I felt tired but also very restless. Couldn't sit still. I had a need to hoover and dust. There was a strange creeping feeling in my scalp, which felt as if little fingers were pulling my hair. I kept running my hands through my hair, but found nothing. These sensations got stronger towards bedtime and around midnight I put out the light to go to sleep when suddenly the doors of my wardrobe started rattling and the building juddered and shook. I felt a frisson of fear. I had just been communing with the Angels and then – Wham! It felt as if there was an energy in the room and everything appeared to be swimming. I heard myself say, "Who is it? If you are of the light you are welcome."

I felt around with my hands and they tingled in the charged atmosphere, which felt full of swirling energy – my imagination? I closed my eyes and my head spun wildly as if I was falling through space. I felt nauseous but then, just as suddenly, was filled with the most beautiful warm orgasmic feeling coming from my lower chakras. My scalp was moving, creeping, more than ever as waves and waves of glorious feelings moved up and down my body. My energy field was being manipulated, pulled one way then another, particularly around the solar plexus. Then the energy around my chest was really buzzing. Every so often, more activity at my scalp and corresponding waves of bliss from my base. This went on and on for a very long time; lots of energy around my throat, then my face and my skin felt hot and prickly. I was awake and fully conscious, but unable to move a muscle. On and on went the waves. I became so tired and drifted in and out of sleep, still with the beautiful waves, still my scalp rippled and my third eye was active till daybreak. Imagine pleading with pleasure to stop.

The next day I was exhausted, my vision swam and I was disorientated and without co-ordination. I learned that the previous night at around midnight there had been an earthquake off the coast of Arran. Did this stimulate my Kundalini? I wrote to Gene Keiffer and he said, "Yes." He had heard of this once before – someone in San Francisco, where earthquakes are quite common. I considered moving there!

He also suggested that this may have been the reason for choosing that house to live in. To him the whole experience seemed significant.

The next entry in my Journal was nine days later and I wrote, 'Dear God, what's happening now?'

I don't know who I am and a sudden panic hits me. Who the hell am I? I can't stop crying because I don't know who I am. Who is living my life? It's totally out of my control. I feel dizzy and disoriented and someone else must be in charge because everything just slips through my fingers. I feel so lost and afraid. There is nothing. What do people think when they look at me? Who do they think I am? Maybe I should ask.

What keeps me here? That's scary because I don't know. Why am I here? I don't know. How can I know when I don't know who I am! I thought, maybe I don't know who I am because I am not in a relationship, but you can't know who you are just because another person is there to look at you. You can't just be the other half of a relationship. You have to be someone in your own right. Have an identity. No purpose, no identity, no reason to be and no strength to get drunk and forget about it.

I ponder this for some days though a bit more calmly. Still trying to figure out how you know who you are if you have no partner as a mirror, I wonder, how do hermits and recluses know who they are? Is that what they seek to know in their isolation? Suddenly, I hear myself say, "That's why you are ill – you don't know who you are and you won't get better till you do know."

I thought of some of the usual spiritual answers: I am part of God; I am a Divine spark; I am a single atom in the Divine body. All clichéd, too abstract, too general, one-size-fits-all sort of answers. I needed personal ones that I could snuggle into and know in my bones that they are for me alone.

Time to sit patiently and ask.

Original Cause

In my past life healing training, the books of Ceanne de Rohan were required reading. They are very unusual and controversial, and are about the origins of all energy. Perhaps best read as metaphor, but they were the prompts for my next meditation on the subject of having no identity.

I asked to be shown my 'original cause' and took myself back to the beginning of earthly time when I saw myself as a cave woman – ferocious and hairy with sharp teeth and long claw-like fingers. "No," I say, "go back to the very beginning," and there I see I am an Angel. But, I see myself pushed out, banished to the sidelines. God has banished me as I sympathized with Divine Mother, who was also banished, and he does not give me a name! I spend a long existence just watching and not taking part. (Er! Hello! sounds familiar!) It is only heart energy that sympathizes or comes near.

So, I ask God now, "Is it ok?"

He says that we are all together now. I see that nothing in creation was whole until the Father and the Mother became One. I see that nothing in me can be whole until my father-mother aspects are one – as above, so below.

God says, "No more blame – mistakes happen in the beginning."

I ask him if I can be given a name now. He says I was Angel Cara of the Heart. My heart had been judged against before. It was good now to be an Angel of the Heart. That is my identity. God himself has named me.

Quite some time later I realize that my Identity issues probably arose following the Kundalini experience. The fire of the Kundalini burns away much of what is no longer useful. In the words of Carl Jung, "When you succeed in awakening the Kundalini so that it starts to move out of its mere potentiality, you necessarily start a world which is totally different from our world. It is the world of eternity."

And that, methinks, is quite a big place.

13

I write in my Journal, 'If we create our own reality, if life is Maya, an illusion, why am I continually creating illness? What am I hiding from?'

I hear the words, "life is too hard," inside my head. Still the same small panicking voice. What is it that is so hard? Why am I not out there fighting? Not that I need to fight, do I? Maybe I believe I need to fight and I don't.

"The world is safe and friendly and all my needs are met," I affirm. I know – I've seen it. Life is created by my own thoughts. I must look at my 'negative lies', the things that have been reinforced time and again. What are they? I sit quietly and contemplate what arises.

In order of the strength of my reaction, they are:

Life is a struggle (thought I'd dealt with that)
I'm not good enough (see useless)
I don't belong (I was banished)
I'm a failure (see useless)

No surprises there then. Same old same old. I will endeavour to explore and clear these negative lies.

Lying in the bath later that day, enjoying the warmth and tranquillity of the water and my candles and music, my mind wanders to thoughts of being in the womb. Suddenly, I gasp for air with a panic and understand that, as my mother was a heavy smoker, I was greatly deprived of oxygen at frequent intervals, thereby enforcing the belief that it was a struggle to

81

live. This feeling that I have of not being able to fully let go and trust must come from here too. How could I relax and be at peace when at any moment oxygen would be taken away? It was never safe to float about and just 'be'. One of my past lives explored in training was ended with the thought that life is hard, and my entry into this life re-enforced that belief.

I have a lot of work to do here. I think I must work on one issue at a time. 'Life is a struggle' is the biggest and, anyway, it surfaced first, demanding to be dealt with.

I lie back in the warm water contemplating the resonance of 'Life is a struggle', which sounds like an echo in my head and the memory of that particular past life healing floods vividly into my mind.

Her last breath had not long left her body and the family were laying my grandmother out on the big kitchen table before the folk of our little hamlet of jumbled houses came to pay their respects. But then, the call came. It was a relief in a way as I always loved the excitement, the danger of our moonlit mission. Besides, a nice little keg of rum would give my grandmother a great send-off.

It was a perfect full moon in a clear sky and as I ran, tucking up my skirts to free my long strong legs, I took the slate steps down, two at a time. My bare feet knew their feel so well. My long curls whipped about my face, caught in the wild sea breezes. I felt alive.

Two little row boats had already landed their load and were heading back to the ship anchored further out in the bay. Everyone in the little cove knew their place and silently kegs and baskets were being passed, one to another. My job was to run up and down the last half of the steps where I then passed them to my brother, who hid them.

The little lamps twinkled. The shush of the waves, the little slaps of the oars, all seemed well, until... I heard, I sensed, I wasn't sure, not till the horses were bearing down on me. I only had time to shout, "It's the King's men," before I was felled.

Who knows how long in that stinking prison? Every moment of every day on guard for my safety, my life. Rumours of prison ships setting sail for the other side of the world. A stinking prison on the sea. I couldn't countenance worse than the one I was already in, but, so it was to be. The filth, the dregs of human misery, led clanking along the boards, the last chance of a deep clean breath before the bowels of hell.

Some spark of survival instinct made me fight my way to a high shelf of wood, just wide enough to lie on sideways. I have to say I bloodied a nose or two but I had it, and before too long knew my good fortune as the floor of the ship grew slimy and fetid with excrement and vomit. Rats not long after. How feral I became. I copied the rats. Very few came near me or challenged me. I survived.

We reached land, but where was I now? The sea was certainly clear and blue and the sand white, but the heat was stupefying. Perhaps that is why I do not have many memories; only chains on my ankles and aching muscles and red raw hands; a hard, hard, existence.

I did have a friend. His name was David. I can't say that I loved him, as that was something that also required some joy, some hope, but companions we were. One day, our chains were removed and we were given a piece of paper saying we were free. We were granted a piece of land, some tools and some seeds and sent on our way. Free.

We set up a makeshift cabin, cleared the red earth and planted. We worked as hard as ever but, plants need water. We gave them our own drinking water, but in the end we all shrivelled. David first. I laid him out on our rough kitchen table just like my grandmother, but with no glass of rum to see him off. Nor even water. I buried him myself.

I was not much longer for that life either and laid myself out on the table and waited ...

* * *

In the healing afterwards when asked, "Looking back on your life, how has it been?" I replied, "Life is just too hard, the struggle too much."

So, it seems I still have a lot of work to do in the here and now.

Rebirthing

Help is at hand. I have been at home, out of the workplace, for quite some time now and have prided myself on the fact that I have not become a daytime TV couch potato. However, a day or two after my 'life is a struggle' episode I do turn it on and there, being interviewed, is an attractive lady talking about rebirthing. Her name is Deike Begg and she is a Jungian-based psychotherapist and astrologer as well as a re-birthing therapist. She has written a book called *Rebirthing: Freedom from your Past.* 'Ding Ding' go the bells in my head, especially when I hear that she lives in the West End of Glasgow. I go to the library, find her book and feel sure that she is my next port of call.

I made an appointment with Deike and felt that all the threads from my previous work were coming together. My chest problems, however, had been getting worse and worse. Perhaps it was subterfuge by my subconscious, but I made it to my first session.

The technique used to enter into the rebirthing process is 'circular breathing' and once into the rhythm of this the energy starts to move. I saw myself in the womb where I was holding on for dear life. I felt as if I was clinging tenaciously, afraid to let go.

"I'll disappear," I said and felt death beckoning. I was afraid, but I wanted to look it in the face. It felt hard to maintain the breathing and I felt myself say, "It's too hard." But I pushed myself on. I could see Jesus in the light and he seemed to be beckoning to me with outstretched arms. I also saw something dark in the womb, curled up at my feet and I was afraid. It wanted me to die! I felt myself declare, "No, I want to live." I wanted to face this dark thing and I challenged it to show its face while I breathed strongly. It felt that the dark thing was a fragment of me that had given up and wanted to drag me into death. It was what was eating up my energy. Gradually, I breathed the dark thing into my body, as I had been taught in 'soul retrieval', working from my feet upwards, explaining who I was to the darkness. When it felt fully breathed in and integrated I felt emotional. I had got my soul back, or so it felt.

Next, there were all sorts of tingles and itches and heat. I breathed into the tension at the base of my lungs and the energy moved to my throat. I now felt it was safe to 'take in' as well as to give out, but then resistance came on with a vengeance and I had huge choking gunge in my throat and my sinuses were blocked. I thought I would throw up – ah ha, it's not safe to speak! I breathed through that till I felt calm and then I felt power coming in.

"I am a strong and powerful woman," I affirmed and huge anger surged upwards against all the men in all my lives who subdued, controlled and judged me. I would no longer give away my power. My lower chakras glowed.

At the end of our session, Deike went off to make some tea to help me come back to earth. She put on some music and it was one of my favourite pieces from 'Songs of the Auvergne' and I cried and cried – hot, fat, effortless tears. I felt as if I had all of myself back and I felt such love for myself. Instead of feeling that I was not 'enough', I knew that I was definitely more than enough for me. Happy tears.

Following on from that, I felt I wanted to practise receiving from the Universe and being comfortable knowing that it was ok to receive as well as to give. I affirmed this to the Universe and less than one hour later I received a phone call inviting me to lunch. I am given a beautiful bunch of roses and homemade jam and soon after that another friend phones to say she is sending me healing!

I am not so good at receiving, so thought I would ask for help. I ask to meet with the one most able to help and suddenly a beautiful presence appears. I hear, "Lakshmi, Goddess of Abundance. She is calm and lovely, peaceful and joyful. She gladly gives. "All is love," she laughs. "The Universe gives gladly. Physical energy, material wealth, laughter, love. Just ask. Be open. Most of all, be open and receive. No stress. No striving. Accept with loving gratitude. Give with loving gratitude."

Peaceful and joyful – that is the feeling. She is very beautiful. Cream and pink. Lotus flowers and pink petals everywhere. She has long dark hair and creamy skin. She sits cross-legged and nearby is a fountain of tinkling water and huge terracotta containers of water full of floating petals. Ease…

Thoughts on Being Human

Something I've been thinking of for a while. If we see ourselves as 'spiritual beings' here on earth for a human experience, rather than human beings searching for a spiritual experience, how will that change our attitudes? Will it, for example, help us realize that our job or our handicap or our poverty is not *who* we are but only the experience we are going through? Will it help us take responsibility for our own human experience and help us see others doing the same thing – can we see others without prejudice of their circumstances? It is only a temporary experience after all.

Will we have more patience with our spiritual seeking if we realize that we are already of the spiritual realms, only seeking contact to help us continue our human experience? If this is so, why do we strive to be spiritually enlightened while we are here on earth? What is it that is so necessary about the human experience and the struggle that we come back, time and time again, into our physical constraints and leave behind that which we seek? "Better to travel hopefully than to arrive!"

Would it mean that we would try harder in this life so that we might be promoted in the next one or, conversely, live a life of selfish indolence hoping we can make up for it next time?

Friedrich Nietzsche said, "My doctrine is: Live that thou mayest desire to live again – that is thy duty – for in any case thou wilt live again!"

At this stage in my search for answers, I feel comfortable saying that non-judgment of others, self-responsibility and awareness of our own part in the Great Plan must have a significant effect on how we live our lives. We do the best we can, in full awareness. That is its own reward. That becomes answer enough.

My Journal:

Last night's dream, telling me I still have time to change. Change what? I have been feeling so unwell, so despairing and negative. I certainly need to change something. Attitude? Yes, probably. I feel as if I have no faith left, either in myself or Spirit or any other person or therapy to make me well. I feel that it has to be me that makes myself well, but I don't have faith in my body's ability to do this. I have faith that other people can do this for themselves and I encourage it. I encourage others to have faith in Spirit, faith in the workings of Spirit – all is as it should be, etc. and yet I cannot seem to do this for myself. I am a fraud! I am mouthing words for other people. How can I do that anymore when I can't have faith for myself? This is serious. Is this the test? I plead with Spirit, the Angels, Archangel Michael, anyone I can think of – please help me! Make me strong and well OR show me how to do it OR show me why I am not well. What do I hear? Nothing! What do I see? Nothing! How deeply can I dig down? I feel such despair. What will sustain me if I have no faith?

I know I have been this low before but it happens more and more easily – I hit what feels like rock bottom and the reasons for coming back up seem so hard to find. I cling (that sounds familiar) to the littlest thing, the teeny weeniest bit of laughter or joy I can find. So damn grateful for anything I can say "There, it's not so bad" to. A drowning woman. Definitely not waving!

A drowning woman? Aha! There are clues in the words we use. Drowning, swamped, overwhelmed – all words I have used lately to describe myself. Clinging on. What is it that is drowning me? Why am I overwhelmed? Drowning is immediate. Am I looking for someone to save me? A handsome lifeguard wouldn't hurt. Am I drowning in the birthing waters? Time to phone Deike Begg for another rebirthing session?

14

Heaven?

Noon and I urgently need to meditate. I quickly go to my tree in the orchard where giggling angels appear, lift me (a bit haphazardly) and transport me to another tree – a palm tree on a white sandy beach where the sea is turquoise and clear. A turtle slowly emerges from the sea.

"I am in heaven," I hear myself say. My idea of heaven? I start to wonder if this is what heaven would be like and, if so (and if I had the choice), would I stay here on earth, on this cold grey place of humanity, or would I go right now to heaven?

What is heaven anyway? It seemed I was being shown the chakras of the earth and what I was giving the name heaven to was the spiritual level or highest chakra of the earth. I felt the 'seventh level' (earth's highest auric field) and all things on earth are mirrored here, or replicated without the lower problems of war, violence, anger and greed – How God meant for earth to be, how we could live, in His beneficence when our consciousness aspires to seventh level.

So, do we need to die in order to attain that? Can we reach seventh level only through meditation while we are still in a physical body or is it all a state of mind? Believing is seeing. Is the paradise I saw there for me if only I change my consciousness? If I am filled with 'lower level' thoughts is that all I will perceive and, conversely, if I *see* heaven on earth is that where and what I will perceive?

In theory, that sounds like what we are told by those who seemingly know, but is that hopeful sentiment? How do I change my cold physical existence into one of heavenly warmth and tranquillity? Do I pack up and go find paradise or do I transform what I have into a new way of perceiving?

In *Beautiful Road Home*, White Eagle says, "There is that within your breast which intuitively longs for heaven."

Is there a correlation between non-acceptance of where I am geographically located (i.e. where my physical existence takes place) and the physical problems I have? Are my physical problems due to the fact that I'd rather be in the heaven that I saw? I have asked the same questions before in different guises and the answer has been that I have difficulty being here and that I have to find ways of bringing joy and reward and 'reasons to be' to keep me grounded. 'Reasons to be' has always been an issue because of my health problems. If I can't be of service or take part in life then there is no reason to be – I see – that's why I get so angry with Spirit. If I have to be here on earth, I should have a reason. Surely, I'm here for a purpose, to make a difference. If not, I'm being kept out of paradise for no reason and therefore it's a punishment. Would I have volunteered to leave paradise and come back to earth if I hadn't had a very good reason?

So tell me, why should I strive here in an earthly existence feeling like I have no reason and no purpose and I am lonely and miserable in this cold place, with poor health, not able to work or play? Couldn't I just end it all and find my way back to heaven? Show me reasons for being here. Show me quickly!

There followed nights of dark and scary dreams. Horribly deformed people rising up in front of my face, attacks by laughing, snapping, slobbering creatures. I run, I fight, resisting the menace, but feel terrorised. Then, a great feeling of power as I defiantly take control, huge and roaring, I slay those who sought me harm, ending with using a toilet in a public street, which had no walls or doors and, not only that, it was more than a wee wee! Yes!!

Rebirthing Session 2

This session was very different from the first. It was not emotional. No blubbing. Instead, lots of strong shifting of energy and a good breathing rhythm, which felt powerful and peaceful. I felt as if I would levitate off the bed and float away. I also felt a deep connection with Archangel Michael and his loving pink energy.

I had talked with Deike about my feelings of drowning and she suggested that I allow these feelings of letting go, but letting go to someone or something above. I liked that idea (letting go and being awash in the sea), but having a lifeline to Divine Mother or Jesus. Meanwhile, energy shifting continued and my face, eyes and throat were twitching. There were stitches in the area of my heart, although I still felt quite blissful. I drifted towards seeing myself floating and freefalling in pink energy, which at first I thought was candy floss, but then saw it was pink feathers. I was floating in them, on them, and they were over me, keeping me warm. Soft, safe love.

When the session was over and I sat up, having tea, I told Deike about the experience I had had, seeing Jesus, in our first session. I explained about the small dark thing I saw and how I thought it was part of me that had split off that I should reintegrate. She said I should not have breathed the lost, dark think back into me and that I should have let it go with the out breath. She said not to integrate anything like that – maybe she was right. Maybe a soul retrieval was not appropriate. She also said that often we start off in the womb as twins, but one dies at a very early stage. Mmm!

This session helped me to clarify some thoughts on letting

go, giving in, surrender, acceptance and just being that have plagued me for so long.

Letting go, or letting *it* go, is a conscious, positive choice. Rather than holding on, nursing and allowing something to ferment, I can let go and move on.

'Give up or give in' is the opposite. This is negative. 'I can't make it better therefore I'm defeated and diminished and I give in'. There is a whole world of difference.

Realizing this, I've made peace with surrender. I just let it go while acceptance now seems so small in the scheme of things. Acceptance means it just *is*, and now when I think of just being I am reminded of the words, "He also serves who only stands and waits." Just being is still useful.

That feels so much better. I slot peacefully back into my centre, ready to start a new day.

15

Today in my meditation I see Divine Mother as a huge heartbeat. She is amorphous and wraps herself around the one needing love, letting her heartbeat warm and heal. She is deep blue. She is the darkness that nurtures and allows all to grow, without judgment – let it be. The divine triangle: God above, holding all together in his golden rays, Divine Mother to his right and Jesus on the other side, white and pale blue and glowing gentleness and compassion. I felt myself in the centre of the triangle – lovely. I felt as if a darkness had been lifted and changes were under way – time will tell.

Later that night I felt full of conflict and many emotions surfaced. I realized that I was afraid to be well. When I thought of being well, I panicked. I so much wanted to take part in life and yet I was afraid. I just wanted to be left alone. I felt as if I couldn't deal with life or relationships. I needed to find my own masculine energies. Maybe look at male archetypes. Need to do something!

Eventually, I slept and I dreamt that I had two or three cars that were all falling apart and I was worried. Then, I decide to use my good car, which was a white sports car. "Why?" I ask myself, "have you been using old cars when you have this lovely one hidden away? Why have you been hiding behind a façade of 'poor' when all the time you have riches?"

Is this relevant to my feelings of being afraid to be well? Do I want people to see 'poor' me? More work to be done.

Thoughts on Recreating Myself

I have been reading Neale Donald Walsch's *Conversations with God*, which hits a lot of spots, particularly about 'creating' ourselves and recreating what we do or do not want to experience. I have been trying to get a clear picture of what I want to create and it's still fuzzy. I do see that I have created almost a victim role for myself and I no longer wish to experience that. I also discover that I have been writing about what I don't want, or about feelings of loss and lack. Now that I realize that, I can change these to positives and a new list of 'recreating myself' grows. Another thought: It takes courage to give up the role of victim. If I can't hide behind my chronic health problems it means I have to take responsibility for what I want or what I don't want. "I am a strong and powerful woman," I again affirm to myself, and I see that I am still caught up in a role of what will other people think. After all I have been through and all I have learned, I still have not let go of that. It is how I feel/think about myself that is important. But this is another can of worms. I question my motives for the need to be of service. Am I seeking an identity that is not mine? Am I trying to gain brownie points in the hereafter? Am I not enough just as I am? Oh no, another maelstrom.

In the next couple of months I affirm loud and clear, over and over, "I am a strong and powerful woman. Everything that comes my way I deal with," and in turn I find that lots of situations are arising that demand truth and emotional honesty from me. When I do say my piece (peace) I feel a great weight lift and I do feel more powerful. However, it looks like the price I have to pay may be losing friends. I have lost one friend and hurt the feelings of another. It's a hard lesson sometimes, speaking your truth.

My Journal:

Yesterday had been one of those strange days when my crown and base centres had been active and my scalp crawling and I had the sense that something was going to happen.

Today, I feel directed to put on 'Spirit of Rainforest' music and after doing my exercises I sit to meditate. I ask to reclaim all of my power, from the beginning of my time and I find myself in the company of an Australian Aborigine medicine man. I have seen him before, briefly, but this time he is covered in grey ash.

All the tribe were there and he was dancing around the fire. He is tall and slim and carries a huge, thick stick with a knob at the end, which he bangs on the earth as he moves around the fire, feet stamping. I felt the people were afraid of him. I sensed the young girls had been mastered by him and were dominated and afraid. There was anger within the dance of this medicine man. It was as if I was being shown this to question me. "Is this the power you want?"

I replied, "Yes." And then heard, "He has anger. He has been guilty of using the young girls. Do you want this?"

I said, "He did, yes, but that's how it was then. He had to be fierce to protect them from the other medicine men and their magic. The energy was of the earth. He was feared and revered, but he was not wrong or bad, as we see it now. I can use this energy, transform it. I can bring in the Divine. I need earth energy too."

He was one of my very early incarnations. I asked him if he would pass on his knowledge to me. We sat facing each other over the fire and he directed me to hold my arms across the fire and take hold of his. We slowly stood up, still holding arms and I had to walk over the fire to him. We then sat opposite each other creating one aura. The people stood around us. I stared into his eyes. I saw his face, which was slimmer and finer than I would have thought, with high cheekbones. I ask his name and it sounds like 'Woomeroo'. I say that I shall call him Spirit of Woomeroo.

He asked for a gift in return and a sick baby was put in my arms. I instantly thought of Jesus and asked him to be with me to heal this child, and he was, and the fever left the child. The people were grateful and gave me their approval. I felt a cord between Woomeroo's hara and mine. He seemed to be saying I should dance in the earth's energies. The hara is said to house the Chi, the vital life force, in the Chinese energy system. Other philosophies call this area the sacral chakra or spleen centre. It is said to be 2 fingers' width below the navel. The energy of the hara is also used in earth or energy healing..

In the crowd of people I was drawn to a very old woman who had only one tooth in her upper palate. Her eyes were loving and warm. Ah, I sense, she was my mother – the mother of Woomeroo! We embraced. I felt safe and warm in the tribe – my back was protected. I was respected for my power. However, I also felt alone. I had had relations with the young girls but no partner, no intimacy – an issue I still have now and am feeling most deeply. I felt myself thinking, 'So, it goes all the way back to then.' Is that why I am feeling such a deep deep need, which borders on anguish, for intimacy? Will this insight help me overcome my patterns and find intimacy in this life?

A busy time. Next morning I am directed to put on 'Spirit of India' music to exercise and meditate to and I wonder why. As I start my exercises I see in my mind's eye a young Indian woman that I had seen before, in the same meditation as I first saw Woomeroo many years ago.

As soon as I sit down to meditate (having found myself dancing, Indian style, before I finished my exercises), I am off to an Indian village. There is a man dancing at a fire and the whole village is watching. He is incredible. He is overwhelmingly powerful and magnetic and I hear myself say, "Let him choose me. Please let him choose me."

I am a young woman, hair in a pigtail, wearing blue sari and trousers and I have little cymbals on my fingers. I want to go and dance with him and I do. He beckons me forward. I can hardly breathe in his presence; he is so powerful and I know I will follow him wherever he goes. I look back at my mother and father and my heart is so sad. I know I must leave them and I can't help it.

Though I follow this man I am sad, not happy. I already know it is doomed, but I am helpless. We travel a long way before stopping at a huge tent. He is cruel. He rapes me. He is a very powerful healer and people come from all over the land with their sick babies and old people and I help him with the herbs. I also dance the sickness out. I see myself with little cymbals on my fingers and bells around my ankles and I whirl and stamp around the sick people, chasing out the sickness.

But, he is still a cruel man who uses me. He starts to collect other young women and I am jealous and decide to use the herbs and spices to poison him and then poison myself. My name is Aisha. My life is tragic and short.

I ask Spirit of Aisha now if I may use her power and knowledge. I say, "No, I don't want to misuse them," and I see clearly how these powers and this knowledge can be misused. "But," I say, "Aisha was so young and so pure and she did all she knew how. I am not so young or inexperienced. I have help and I take full responsibility for this power and knowledge, which I will use in her honour. I will always remember how she died."

She takes me to see the herbs growing and then shows me all the dried herbs and spices in copper bowls. She gives me written instructions, in cuneiform, to read. She shows me her dance. I ask if I can see my mother and father again and we go back to the village and I kiss them both, still feeling sad, especially about leaving my mother. As we look into each other's eyes we say, "See you next time," and we smile. She was the mother of Woomeroo as well and I believe the same soul as my mother in this lifetime. Our connection is strong.

I also cut cords with that powerful man. I see a huge thick cord attached to my solar plexus, like strong rope used to tie up a ship. It is so thick I have to use a caustic solution to burn it. There are other smaller cords which I deal with until I am sure he is gone completely.

Aisha was so lovely. Young and pretty and vulnerable. I can use her power and knowledge in recompense for her short, sad life.

Both of these meditations leave me with questions. Why was I shown them? The connection seems to be lessons in misuse of power or knowledge, but I don't know why I need to be shown this as I really can't see myself doing this. Was it another way of reminding me that we have all we need already: all the skills, all the power, all the knowledge? We can draw on these if and when needed? Is it about discrimination? Be careful what you wish for? A strong and clear message is not always immediate. I will have to see how they fit into the great scheme of things.

Swimming in the Sea of Love

Today in meditation I am aware of Jesus. I am at his feet and he blesses me and wants me to stand and look at him. He is so beautiful. He puts a hand on my head in blessing as I kneel. When I stand he embraces me. He leads me by the hand and we sit by the side of what seems to be a pink sea with beautiful golden-haired children happily bobbing up and down. He tells me that this is what the souls of everyone look like. This is how we truly are. I see then that it is a Sea of

Love and all the souls are like frothy waves. Everything is free and weightless. Jesus suggests I dive in and I do. I freefall into the Sea of Love. I dive and swim and tumble in great joy, as does everyone else. It seems that everyone is there.

I then take this image of the Sea of Love and superimpose it over my surroundings here in Glasgow, so that I see the street I live in through layers of pink (like fine candy floss). I feel I'm being shown that I should view the world as a Sea of Love and all the people as souls swimming in it. Freedom and weightlessness. No struggle. Lovely.

I remember in Gopi Krishna's book, recounting the after effects of his Kundalini experience, he says that everything he saw seemed to be covered in a fine white dust. He found this most disturbing and disconcerting. I wonder what it would be like to walk around, every day of your life, sun or rain, and see the world through pink candyfloss. Is this where the term 'rose-tinted glasses' comes from? I must remember to have such glasses handy to use, like a hero in a children's story. I will put on my magic glasses to make it all better.

16

I have been visiting Morning Light in the North of Scotland and I drive from there to Pluscarden Abbey in Morayshire. The day and the scenery were beautiful and when I arrived at Pluscarden I was directed to the women's quarters: little bedrooms, communal kitchen, sitting room and communal showers. I was welcomed by two women already ensconced there and then I met Brother Finbar who was a delight. He is from the south side of Glasgow like me, and has a sense of humour right up my street. My heart soared when I heard the bells for vespers and I rushed up to the church, and again at 8.05 p.m. for compline, not knowing anything at all about the services. I felt out of place with the women, but I was so at peace with the plainsong of the brothers and the sparse surroundings and in bed that night I was so peaceful, I thought I would float away.

The brothers have a very simple life, working in the gardens or with the bees, ever ready to down tools when the bells ring for prayers. But what I found amazing was their wonderful sense of humour. There is a little shop, which works on the 'honour' system: take something and leave the money. All around the walls of the little shop were cartoons which mostly poked fun at themselves.

I stayed for a couple of days and, although reluctant to leave the peace of Pluscarden, I decided to move to Findhorn. On the way I stopped at Cluny Hill College, Forres, to call in on someone I knew. I had been very curious about the place, and had previously thought of going to stay there. However, after a short time, I felt bored by the atmosphere and was anxious to move on to Findhorn.

It had been an ambition for a long, long time to visit Findhorn, but once there I found it all very strange – all those hippy types – and suddenly I was depressed. I felt I didn't fit in anywhere. Why was that? Was I being too judgmental or was I not willing to fit in? Persevering, I went into the pottery workshop and there was a huge bowl of Angel Cards. I picked one and laughed – it was 'flexibility'.

I stayed for a couple of days, met someone I knew, but the feeling of not belonging was too strong. I felt jaded. I felt as if I had outgrown the people I met there. Was this sour grapes? I wanted to understand so I wandered about a bit more, enjoying the beautiful countryside, chatted with more people and went to a fantastic concert in Universal Hall, but no – not for me. I conclude, at last, that I want a no frills route to spirituality. I see the brothers at Pluscarden this way. Uncluttered and unfettered. I see Findhorn, Clunie and all the 'New Age' as packaging – fancy packaging and all the seekers caught up in the wrapping.

I know I don't want dogma and I see the New Age way can be another form of dogma. 'My way will get you enlightenment'. 'My way will make you well'. I feel that sometimes they are as guilty of disempowering as organized religion. The truly spiritual person does not seek to recruit or convert and offers advice only when asked. At one time I needed the New Age glamour to help me appreciate that I needed Spirit in my life, but I feel I have now shed the need for glamour. I know I must learn non-judgment and patience with those taking the New Age route – all roads lead to the Godhead after all – and, at the same time, enjoy my own path. This sounds critical of Findhorn and I don't mean it to be. It is a fantastic achievement born of the highest ideals and has helped countless people upon the path. It is just that, it is no longer for me.

Archangel Rafael and the Mystic Rose

I had been reading Diana Cooper's book, *A Little Light on Ascension*, and I thought I would investigate some new angels. I had tried before to feel a connection with Archangel Rafael, who is the healers' angel after all, but had not been successful. So I tried again.

In my meditation I go to my meadow, sit under my tree and wait. I see a beautiful rose and hear the words, "Mystic Rose." The rose becomes clearer; it is perfect, open and pale pink. Rafael (was it Rafael?) speaks to me saying that this is my image. All was perfect. Did a rose strive to be more perfect? More beautiful?

He said that this open mystic rose was the symbol for the earth – perfection in the eyes of God. I looked into the rose and it was stunning, with tiny droplets of water on the petals.

Rafael said, "Tears, just like rain on roses makes the perfume stronger," and he told me again that there was no need to strive. Just be.

I try to 'just be'. Not easy for me, but as I hit a bad M.E. time I must try to practise this. I notice that I have a tolerance level. After a couple of weeks of feeling ghastly, depression sets in. I am able to manage the first big attack, which can happen at any time without warning. But I know for a day or two, maybe more, I'll be in a state of blobdom, so I cancel my life. Thereafter, although much constrained, I am still hopeful that in another day or two I'll be fine. I start to accept social invitations, so joyful am I about the possibility of life restarting. Then, so dumped do I become when I realize I still have a long road to go to recovery.

But this is when I write it out. These writings are not things of beauty. They can be full of moaning and bitching. I get a large piece of paper and a pencil (a pencil moves faster on the page). I pick a time when I will not be interrupted. I will not answer the phone or the door. I sit with paper and pencil till the energy starts to move and then I write. I write the first thing that comes into my head and do not stop till the anger, frustration, fear or whatever is completely gone. I may be crying, coughing or spluttering during this process, but not by the time I stop. By then, I feel so relieved and empty and ready to start life anew. Fantastic! I do not correct my grammar – no dotting of i's or crossing of t's. Plus, very importantly, I do not reread what I have written. I have written it out of myself and I do not want to take any of it back in again. Shred it up and throw it away and start all over again…

Janice Galloway, a Scottish author, wrote a book called *The Trick is to Keep Breathing*. I actually saw it as a play some years ago and I remember it as being a sensitive and humorous portrayal of mental health problems, but it is the title that particularly stuck with me. I have repeated it countless times, either through sobs or laughter. "That's it, Carol. Try another breath. Jolly good. Keep them coming," etc.. Thank you, Janice Galloway.

Shinto – Be an Empty Vessel

Still having a bad M.E. time, I go to bed and listen to a music tape. I am immediately transported to an Oriental garden and in front of me is an Oriental man, Japanese I think, but I'm not sure. He has straight black hair and is wearing a long cream-coloured tunic with wide sleeves. His arms are folded, hands inside the sleeves. He beckons me to follow him and we go to a building where the walls are also doors and they slide open easily and noiselessly. He takes me into a very simple room with an altar, but there is nothing on the altar. I ask where we are and he replied, "Shinto." He then bows in front of the altar, looks at me and says, "Carol, you must be as the empty vessel. Let your vessel be cleansed." I then feel, rather than hear that I should forget all I know and start again.

Before this happened I was so downhearted that I had been saying to myself, "I give up." If there is anyone 'there' they would have to do it – I'd had it!

I knew nothing about Shinto, so later I found a book at the library. Apparently, it is Japanese and was their main religion before Buddhism. Shinto worships nature and the power of nature. Didn't know that.

After learning about Shinto and wondering about being an empty vessel, I repeatedly picked up references to Zen and also to Zen's 'don't know mind'. I also found a story about a successful businessman who becomes very interested in Zen Buddhism and finds himself a master with whom to study. He goes on retreats for long periods of time and after every retreat his master sets him the question, "What is enlightenment?" But the man never knows the correct answer, no matter how hard he strives. This process goes on painfully for a long time and, eventually, after many years, when the master asks him the question the man replies miserably, "I don't know!" The master claps his hands in glee and says, "Congratulations. *Enlightenment is* 'don't know mind'."

Here is something to work with. That gladdens my heart.

A Major Breakthrough in Love

I had another rebirthing session, but this time I felt ghastly. In my opinion, I over-breathed, left my body and could not get back in. I couldn't stand up straight. I was wobbly and 'listing to starboard'. I was so dizzy and nauseous for some days that I could not get out of bed. This left me with too much time to brood. My thoughts returned to my ex-lover and how, after three years of being apart, I still felt pain. I closed my eyes to contemplate and the realization rushed over me – I have been trying to let go of the love that I felt for him so that the pain would go away, while all the time I should have been letting go of the pain and accepting that love is still there.

The jaggy pains in my heart got worse at this thought, but I sent love to the hurt and the hurt lessened. I saw that if I felt I didn't know why this had to be, the pain would diminish. This has been a huge lesson, a soul lesson in non-attachment and unconditional love. This is a gift. This is freedom to love without pain, without the need for it to be given back. This is a major breakthrough. I no longer need to be free of love or my lover.

P.S. I can't wait to tell you that my lover came back into my life five months later. Permanently!

17

Stream of Consciousness and other Meditations

I am anxious to get on with some writing and decide to try asking for a muse to come and help me. I sit and meditate and I go to a place where there are rocky hills behind me, a secret place with a small river meandering, curving and looping through the rocky landscape. It is a very small river, maybe more of a stream, and there are things floating in it. It's running fast and I hear myself say, "It's my stream of consciousness." With this realization, I'm aware that maybe I should be observing what is floating past.

I see a house on its side go past. I see a dragon. A dragon? I dismiss this, but still I see the dragon looking at me, slightly panic-stricken and definitely surprised. I run after it, following the fast-moving water until it comes to a place where large rocks narrow the passage of the stream and I'm able to help him out. He seems very grateful. I invite him back to where I was sitting and ask him why he's in my consciousness. He says he's fed up with being feared and not befriended. He wants me to be with him and to listen to him. He says his fire can help me in my writing. He has passion, he says – the fire of passion. He can lick the bones of ideas clean with his fire and I can clothe them. He seems altogether shaken up by his tumbling down the stream experience, so we just sit companionably and watch what else goes by. There is some furniture, a jumble of people. Then my old boss goes past a couple of times and so does my lover. The sun and the moon pass, as well as a boat and the words, "The cargo of my boat is love, washed from shore to shore".

None of this makes any sense, but I liked the idea of watching my stream of consciousness. Oh, and by the way, the dragon is called Chang. He is very old and has beautiful turquoise/green/blue scales and wings and he points out that he has five toes, which he assures me is very special.

Enchantment and Butterflies

My meditation had many noise distractions today, but I was really in need of positive feelings, so I focused on the music playing with the sound of water running and wind blowing, and found myself sitting in a deep dark cave. I sat near the mouth of the cave so that I could watch the storm that was taking place. I was filled with joy and my belly was thrilled with excitement – like the feeling I used to get as a child when I was in a caravan and rain would be battering down. A feeling of safety, but also of exhilaration. The cave was comforting and secure and I felt utterly at peace and, for some reason, loved, like a lover was standing close behind me, melded into my back, holding me. I watched the rain and the lightning and I was filled with awe for all of creation. The cave was also inhabited by small creatures sheltering from the storm and I felt so burstingly joyful at the one-ness of nature. My throat chakra was humming pleasantly and my auric space was blue. Suddenly, lots and lots of small yellow/white butterflies burst out of my throat. I was delighted. Then, notes of music tumbled out followed by framed works of art. I saw the *Mona Lisa* go past and I laughed. Long silk scarves of rainbow colours streamed out; lovely blues and pinks. After a short pause a beautiful butterfly slowly fluttered out, hovered for a while then flew off. Quite lovely and I am left feeling that I want to write of enchantment.

The following day in my meditation I open the little door in my heart and set it free. It needs to be soaring far from humankind, far from earthly constraints. It needs to feel utter love, to be with God, Divine Mother, Jesus, All That Is; to feel Divine love and peace. It needs to just soar and soar and tumble and laugh and freefall in pink joyness, like a caged bird set free, not thinking of anything except the joy of freedom. Joy, laughter, bubbling from every pore. Uncontained and uncontainable. This is worth everything.

Such love filling up inside my body, my heart, my head, my eyes. Indescribable joy and yet melancholy too.

"Take me home. I remember Paradise. Take me back. Why was I cast out? How long do I have to stay here? But, for the meantime, just let me soar. Let my heart remember boundless love. Fill it with the fragrance of the Divine – a Divine workout for the heart," says a voice in my heart. I feel it expanding, throbbing, stretching and pulsating and, boy, it needs to be strong and resilient. Even if the rest of me doesn't work, I'll have a strong and pliable heart.

Come back in now, heart. Tell me what you saw. Let me feel you gently throbbing. Tell me how it is in heaven. Why does that make me feel homesick? Full of peace and joy, but also full of longing. It will wait for me, I hear you say. "It knows your longing. Stay here and shine your light."

Do I feel such love because I trust this spiritual love? Do I find myself unable to feel uncontained love in the physical because I don't trust? When you are a child you just love – no sides, no worries, just go for it. When do we learn the barriers? When do we first learn that it's so cold when the sun goes down? Is it possible to recapture that simple trust? In theory, yes; jump right in and to hell with the consequences. Grab whatever love and joy is there, in the moment. Dive into the intensity of it. Plenty of time later for misery. Worse than great joy or sorrow is the constant daily grind of greyness. No hurts, no gains. No enemies, but no lovers. No arguments, but no loving frolics. Not quite starving, but feasting neither.

Here is what I want: feasts and lovers and joyous tumbles. What extravagance of joy! Well, no time like the present… For today, I will laugh as much as I can. I will feel free and able to do anything. Hey, my heart just went to heaven. Where did yours go? I can go anywhere, me and my heart. My heart is strong enough for love, passion and joy. We've got a lot of loving to do. Sorrow, don't wait up for me.

My Journal:

Not such joyous stuff in my journal lately. I had the D's: depressed, despondent, desolate, desperate and down in the dumps. I can't even meditate, so I just sit and sigh. But an unexpected sense of peace washes over me as I realize I am staring at a vase of flowers and am overcome by their perfection. They are so open and generous. They offer all they have. "Here I am. I show you my innermost being, my beauty and my flaws. I don't give or take. I just am. Here till I am here no longer. Feed me, water me, appreciate me and I will be here longer!" How can we not believe in Spirit when all that perfection is contained in a flower, every flower. Perfect unto itself. No evolutionary mistake, no random chaos. Look around, can't you just see gifts and miracles everywhere. Look into a baby's eyes. Don't you see wisdom – how was heaven when you left it? Straight from God's wisdom, through the tunnel of forgetfulness into the harsh light of learning. Again.

I am overcome with wonder. I've gone all mushy and tears stand ready to fall. I'm having an 'isn't the sky so blue' sort of morning – soppy and sentimental and happy to be alive. Yes! You heard it here first: Carol is happy to be alive.

110

A Small Epiphany

There could be two reasons for you to be reading this book: either you think it's interesting, or you think – ooo! – this woman is cuckoo. Frankly, I'm not sure which camp I would follow. After all, why do I do this? Why disappear inside my head then write it all down? What is it that I actually do? I sit quietly and, if I am lucky, a switch is flicked on and off. I surf. Just like the internet. Whoa! Just a minute. Epiphany. I Mind Surf! This is exactly what I do. Oh, I feel so much better with that thought – my own personal questions and answers session. I experience things first-hand. I surf archetypes, angels, power animals, Spirit Guides. I journey or quest with healing guides, look at past lives or early life, speak with my body parts, etc, etc. I look inside my own wisdom instead of taking on the experience of others. True knowledge is experience. I see it, hear it, smell it! I trust it. I can tune in instead of switching on.

Personal experience is the best way to know. Anything less is the filtered-down version of another person's truth. To surf your mind allows insight into who you truly are. You discover more of yourself, the depth and potential. Each time you go within you exercise innate wisdom, stretch your boundaries, which once stretched will never contract to what they used to be. You shine your own light on all the nooks and crannies of potential still shrouded in darkness. Just waiting, waiting, waiting... You are your own confidante, your own counsellor, your own guide. Surf and see!

The human experience *is* to experience. What else is there? Take love for example. You can read about it and that's very nice, but to experience it is the only way to know and feel the aliveness of it, the heat and blood-rushing excitement of it. The sickness and despair and the recovery from it and the headlong dizzying rush into it all over again. Can't get that from a book or a movie or a friend's story.

111

This renews my excitement. I don't just sit here doing nothing. In some ways, it could be argued, I am experiencing more of life than many who are rushing around in the material world. This gives me reason.

Is God the Wizard of Oz?

I have been going to the Philosophy Café in Glasgow and this is great fun. We all disagree with each other but it's all polite. I like that. We listen to one another first. Later when we go for a drink in the bar and it's just as active with more opportunity to interrupt, but we are still polite. Chatting with a chap I find most agreeable, he suddenly confronts me with, "Perhaps God is just a huge ego needing to be fed by human desire. A gigantic sponge."

Well, I was horrified and said so, but of course, during the night, awake in the small hours, these things rear up and make you take notice.

I was also thinking about life. Is it on a 'need to know' basis? Is the spiritual evolution we seek given only on this basis? Is life a big secret? Is God a closely-guarded secret? I suppose so, otherwise wouldn't all the seekers already have found out and told the rest of us. If we did know the 'secret' would we find out that God is actually the Wizard of Oz and life is a huge thunder and lightning machine? Or, even worse, a gigantic ego needing to be fed by human desire to find the secrets or by the human love of a good mystery? The ultimate mystery. Is it all a huge cosmic joke? Are we humans thrown the odd 'coincidence' to make us go 'Wow'? Are they having a laugh, those chaps upstairs, each time another gullible human is ensnared?

"Bring me another human; this one's got cynicism."

Does one cynic make the whole barrel bad? The gullible shall inherit the earth – ha ha!

God a sponge? What sense would there be in that? Or is there any sense? Why do we have to work so hard and for so long to penetrate any of the mysteries? Or is that part of the plan to keep us interested, the mysteries being divine sticks and carrots? We are shown a glimpse, the carrot is near, we run towards it a little faster each time with renewed effort, but – whoosh – we can't quite grasp it. I suppose that if we went direct from questions to answers there would be no journey. There would be no reason to believe the answer if we had not trod the path one step at a time, had a bit of a struggle.

No. I find it impossible that selfish egotism could produce the beauty of nature, babies' laughter, birdsong. I will just go and 'mind surf' to renew my vision of all the beauties, wonders and miracles that are ours. All the love and joy. Anything else is the illusion of all illusions. Or a yellow brick road.

18

Another new year and this one starts rather well. My lover has come back into my life, just when I thought I'd never get through another winter and, incidentally, only a few months since I had let him go, with love.

I met some other chaps on the inner planes as well.

I had been reading Leslie Keaton's *13 Quantum Leaps for the Soul* and thought I'd give one of her methods of meditating a try, reaching the 'upperworlds' by going through a hole in the sky. I imagined a hill in Femes in Lanzarote where people go to watch the sunset as my entry point. Ladders came down and up I climbed. I arrived in a place of white sand, blue sea and angels sitting around, chilling out. I am then told that I have to go somewhere and a huge sea snake appears out of the water. I am not exactly happy about riding on the back of a snake or going under the water and I'm given a mask and oxygen as it's obvious that I am a little afraid. I climb on the back of the enormous sea snake whose skin is more crocodile-like than snake-like. Strangely enough, it is rather pretty, with two little ears and eyes huge as globes with long thick lashes.

We go fast under the water and soon emerge in the mouth of a cave where I meet a very old man with dishevelled long grey hair and beard. He invites me to sit. I tell him my worries as he seems to be interested. He says that help will come from an unexpected source and he repeats this, telling me not to worry. I hear myself call him 'Wizard' and I realize I had been contemplating wisdom before my meditation and as that thought came into my head I saw the connection – WIZard and WISdom. A Wizard is a person of wisdom. Huh! I tell him I really want wisdom, but it seems I still have a lot to learn about love first. I tell him I had never thought of wisdom in terms of being a wizard. He said I already was a wizard, but just didn't realize it. He laughed at my puzzlement and gave me a wand. "You don't really need it, but you may like it," he said. "All Wizards do is change the reality they find themselves in. You can do the same. Create your own possibilities. Change what you don't want." He shrugged and laughed as the sea snake appeared to take me back. He was such a good-humoured wizard that I hoped I'd meet him again. He said I should call him Wiz and he waved me off.

Back on the beach, the angels all looked as if they knew what I had experienced. They grinned and waved me off – what a lovely experience – and very soon thereafter, help did come as Wiz had advised and, yes, I was surprised from where.

The very next day I am quickly up and away above the clouds and the sea snake awaits me. I don't use an oxygen mask this time, just hold my nose. Wiz is waiting and gives me a cup of what he calls 'healing and strengthening tea'. He says he has been reading up on M.E. It is an illness sent (by whom he didn't say) to enable us to test strength of spirit. I don't like that and I turn my head away, but he adds, "How else would you have known your spirit is strong? Your emotional body was tested early and mentally you are quite strong, but the mental and the physical are bound together. You need more focus mentally and the physical will follow."

He holds up a hexagonal disc, black and white, and spins it before my eyes. It is very hypnotic and I feel myself go deeper and in my inner screen, I then find myself sitting opposite Ernest Hemingway in a Parisian café as he sits writing. Even *I* think, "Nah, can't be." However, I understand

I am being shown that I must get back to the mental focus of writing.

I say to E.H, "You were quite a man, weren't you?"

He laughs and says "Yes. When you write you must focus only on writing, but when you live, you must live life to the edge. Focus fully on life and focus fully on writing. No use snuffling around."

I ask, "Who helped you write?" and I see a picture of a man who looks like Wiz but E.H. says he was called Scribe. E.H. also says that I could come for instruction, but that he might not always be sober! He is a huge personality and I like him. He says he has helped others before and then pushes me away, good-naturedly, as he says he has other things to do.

Back to Wiz, who confirms, "Focus, focus, focus. Create your own possibilities." He gives me more tea for the journey home and sea snake takes me back where all the little fairies and twinkling things wave me off again, before I come back down the ladder. I bring back a sense of fun, a busy heart and a great excitement.

Ok, so maybe I need a reality check here, but all I can say is, I was in Paris sitting on a cast iron, wobbly chair, in a café, opposite Ernest Hemingway who was writing and drinking a foul-smelling drink when I dropped in!

The Land of the Lost Libido

I feel the need to sit and meditate. I feel peaceful but also strangely excited. I choose some music and I pick a crystal to hold. My heart is fit to bust with good feelings of gratitude and I want to express this in my meditation. However, I find myself at the bottom of a ladder leading heavenward. I climb up to the clouds, which seem so like candyfloss. I find a latch and push open a hatchway and climb. The first thing I see is a fat little cherub eating the clouds. It *is* candyfloss! I laugh and say, "No wonder you are all fat little cherubs." I see lots of different forms all sitting or lying around and eating or drinking, and it feels very lazy, luxurious and sensual.

I am drawn to a beautiful creature who is lying on his side, propped on his elbow (elbow?). His back is actually covered in exquisite feathers of the palest pink: huge wings which look so soft they might melt. He beckons me to lie down. He is the most beautiful man I have ever seen.

I hear myself whisper, "Adonis." He has blonde curly hair, an exquisite face, perfect body, but above all sensuality oozes from him.

I hear, "This is the Land of the lost Libido," and I laugh and say that I lost my libido ages ago! He covers my body with his wings, very gently, almost touching but not quite, starting from my head, down.

This is not sexual but immensely sensual. I hear myself gasp. Smaller creatures caress my body with sweet-smelling oils. Every cell of my body is in bliss. There are fruits to eat and nectar to drink. I lower myself into a pool of water and float in complete surrender and when I emerge I see myself as a beautiful, light-filled woman. My skin is completely unblemished, my hair is long and full of light and I am wearing a dress of cloth that is so exquisite on my body that all I can do is gasp with the bliss. I see now that there are other people around the pool, each with a divine creature leaning at their side. Bliss everywhere. Every part of me is in bliss and I don't want to leave. My divine creature tells me that the way I saw myself when I emerged from the pool is how he also sees me. That was my essence. He is giving me back my sensuality. He says, "It is God's gift. It is for pleasure. Pleasure should be enjoyed. It is an expression of God." Wow!

The other people start to leave and I think, *Well, I was here last, I'm leaving last…* Don't want to go, but eventually I float away on happiness.

Merging with my Animus

There were bound to be changes in my thought processes after that experience. Three days later, after many dreams about me taking control and having more male energy, I sat to meditate. I first of all went looking for my quartz crystal, which I often like to hold, and as soon as I sat there were fireworks, sharp small explosions, and I see a man wearing a golden cape, like a circus performer: a Brothers Karamazov character. He has black, slicked-back hair, black moustache and so much energy that everything is crackling and popping. He is in a huge dark space and is acting as if he is performing in front of an audience. He sees me and we greet each other. He says to me that he has "too damn much testosterone".

I say, "Well, maybe I can help." Though I wasn't sure how. But we agree that it is possible we can help each other. He is my Animus.

I ask, "In what way do you think I can help?"

He replies that he needs to find some peace, some ability to be quiet and tender and not popping and exploding all the time.

We give it some thought and agree that as he has too much energy and I don't have enough, perhaps we could exchange. We also agree that sexual union is the preferred route. We stand and look at each other feeling very awkward, and I say, "Well, how do we do this?"

He replies briskly that he is the Animus, the aggressor, so he should "take me". He tries this, very passionate, like Errol Flynn in a love scene and I just burst out laughing, which really hurts his pride.

I say, "No, no. I realize you are the aggressor and I am the feminine, but maybe I can help here. I'm the Anima and I'll receive your excess energy, but let's slow down." So, I have him lie down beside a little stream and I bathe him. At first this is quite mechanical, but then as I start to oil his muscled back and buttocks and I look at his beautiful male body I become aroused. Oh ho! Seems I do have my libido back. I turn him over and he has a huge erection. I lower myself onto him and it is *so* beautiful – an overwhelmingly sensual and erotic experience. I gasp with the powerful feelings. Our bodies start to melt into each other. We are all legs and arms tightly wrapped around each other and we float off into the cosmos. We are in the star-ridden skies. We are in the ocean. We are wrapped together in the snow. We are covered in blossoms falling from trees. Completely! Wow! We hold our foreheads together to merge our minds and my inner space is purple.

I hear myself say, "I am You and You are Me. You are my Merge. Now I am complete."

I want to stay there. I feel peaceful. I feel barrel-chested. I feel filled out. When I do open my eyes, I realize my crystal is phallic-shaped and I laugh. I feel different. I told Him I wanted to be unafraid. I wanted to be strong and make my way in the world. I need to project. Can I retain some of his 'crackle and pop'?

I don't know if all this male energy helped me or not, but I note that in my inner world, at least, I am no wimp.

Not all my meditations and journeys, or my dreams, are filled with beauty and joyful inspiration. I have some dark and scary times too. Very scary. Lurking-in-the-shadows scary. I have felt terrified at times, but at some point I stop being afraid and instead I 'face the demon' and roar. Not allowing myself to be dominated by fear, I challenge the dark things and they crumble and become small scared things who have lost their way. Then, shown the light of compassion, they seem happy to move on, bullies no more.

A Course in Miracles says that the opposite of love is fear. If we flood the darkness with love instead of fighting and challenging, the dynamics completely change. Fear and darkness melt and disappear.

* * *

My adventures in the 'invisible worlds' always remain very vivid in my mind. Sometimes, years later, I may read or learn something new, which triggers memories of one of these adventures and may shed more light on them. For instance, I have been fortunate enough to find The School for the Study of the Seven Rays and the inspiring and encouraging teacher there, Kurt Abraham. In the 'SS7R Newsletter' (Vol.10, No 3, 2008), there is a fascinating article on 'The Tabula Smaragdina' by Gautam Doshi, which illuminates many experiences and trails of thoughts for me. On the subject of my crackle and pop man, I learn that the ancient Egyptians believed that sex is wisdom, as the union of masculine and feminine on the higher planes synthesizes knowledge and brings enlightenment. It is a liberation from the male/female dichotomy. It is a realization of 'I am One' (and perhaps, therefore, I can create, I am enough). The Egyptians also regarded the next stage after this union as union with the 'overself', when Spirit and Soul unite in the higher state of consciousness called 'The Intelligence of the Heart'.

So, my Animus – not a one-night stand then!

I had another tête à tête with Ernest, who gave me some more advice about being fully present and 'smelling the dust' when writing, and I still meet up with Wiz. In fact, I flew to him after the 9/11 bombings.

"I don't want to be part of this humanity," I cried. But he persuaded me to stay as part of the human family then he sent me off with an angel, way up high above the planet into a space filled with giant computer screens and keyboards. The angel tapped in some things and there I was, on the screen, a trudging dark little figure, all huddled over, all gloom and dragging feet. I recognized myself and understood that I'm beyond all help when I'm in that state, closed to the Universe, closed to everything except my own misery. I laughed when I saw this and realized how self-destructive I can be. No energy able to get in or out. Hey, I forgot about JOY!

I thanked the angel for showing me the 'viewing room' and returned to Wiz feeling a little bit sheepish at my behaviour.

"Do it in struggle or do it in Joy – it's the same lifespan," he gently reminded me.

I know, I know. I get it.

A New Playmate

One more chap comes into my inner life when I learn 'symbolic sight' at my friend Maureen Lockhart's workshop. He is a huge figure of a man, dressed all in silver – silver cloak and silver boots that thunder towards me.

"Hey," I say. "You're just like Flash Gordon," and we both laugh.

Maureen had just shown us a breathing technique that enabled us to see beyond the physical body, into the subtle layers. I had hardly started, but there he was, pulling me out the top of my head.

"Hold on, it's not my turn yet," I laugh, but he is hauling me out and yelling, "Hurry up. I've waited long enough."

I have a very difficult time controlling my giggles. He makes me feel so joyous and leaves me with a warm glow, like being in love! He is very eager to spend time with me.

Over this winter I have a difficult time with asthma and bronchitis and feel quite desperately in need of answers. In reply, I have an urgent need to meditate. I hurry to sit and am immediately up in the clouds. 'Flash' is already there, then the snake appears and rushes us off to Wiz, who is anxiously awaiting us and says we must hurry, that a Great One is talking about asthma and we must go and listen.

We fly upwards to an outdoor auditorium where people are already seated and an old man is standing on a rostrum addressing them. He is very old with long white hair and beard, wearing long white robes. I 'sense' he is Maimonides. He shows us that the lungs are like the tablets that the Ten Commandments are written on and I visualize a Sunday school-type picture of Moses standing, holding the stone tablets and – yes – they are shaped like the lungs! It makes absolute sense to me.

He tells us our lungs contain our own personal command-ments that we agreed upon with God and that anyone with asthma is living outside the agreed commandments. Everyone's are personal and individual.

"How do we find this out?" someone asks.

"How do we know what we are in discord about?" asks another.

He replies, "You must discover for yourselves. You must uncover your own personal commandments and what you are not in accordance with."

A man in the audience asks Maimonides for a demonstration and, to my horror, he points at me to stand. I am most reluctant, but Wiz pushes me and Flash nods his head in agreement. Everyone turns to stare at me.

"What do you see when you look at this one?" asks Maimonides.

"Love and caring," someone said.

"Yes, yes," said Maimonides. "Of course. But what is in discord?"

No one spoke.

Eventually, he said, "The left side is closed. There is fear – fear of being all of whom she should be." Then, to me he said, "Allow God's 'inspiration' to enter. Be inspired. The breathlessness you feel is very high up and near your throat now. You must have free expression, courage to use free expression. It is near to healing."

I thanked Maimonides and spoke to him in person later. I asked him if I could meet with him again, but he said that he was not often this close and that I had to work on my own behalf. He said it was not dragons I had to slay; it was timid, fearful fluttering birds. I had to learn to calm them first then allow them to leave through free expression. Not with a huge roar, but by continuous gentle courage, a little at a time.

We returned to the cave where Wiz gave us one of his brews and we sat for a while, contemplating, before the snake took me back, safe and sound.

Personal Commandments? Sounds serious.

19

I had a night of disturbed dreams, discovering that I judged things from their external appearance. I reluctantly entered an ordinary tenement flat to discover that, at its rear, it had a beautiful view and a swimming pool. I was ashamed for thinking the people who lived there were poor and boring. Was this a lesson in being non-judgmental?

Next, I 'travelled' to find myself looking at shelf after shelf of beautiful books, and I said to someone that I wanted more. I was handed a telephone and told, "Tell her what you want."

I didn't know exactly what that was, so I muttered on and eventually said that what I really wanted was knowledge – esoteric knowledge. There was not much response from the telephone, but quickly I found myself in a small boat.

"Going over the sea," were the words that I heard. There were others in the boat and, when we landed, I was guided to a cave. Again, I should not have judged from the outside, because inside it was large and warm and hung with rich tapestries. There were lots of women studying. I was shown to a big beautiful bed in a corner, where there was also a chair and desk for my books. A beautiful woman in a distinctive headdress and long gown introduced herself to me as the Teacher of Esoteric Knowledge. I heard the name "Hannah" and the other women were referred to as "Sisters" – Hannah and her Sisters? (Ok, Carol, that's the name of a Woody Allen film!)

I was told by Hannah that I could have all knowledge, but was I prepared to dedicate myself to this? I said that, all my sleep time, all my meditation time and more, I would happily devote, but my heart sank at the thought of more isolation. Do I still need to be shut away, studying and learning? Am I not yet ready to be out in the world speaking my truth? When will I find my voice? I reluctantly replied that I would have to consider this.

The Soul Robber

I had things to consider in the 'real world' too. Finances being desperate, I had to think about finding a flatmate. I advertised at the university and a young French woman came to view the room. She was a strange, unfortunate-looking girl and I heard myself say to her that she could come and share. Later, however, when she left, I felt disturbed and depressed. She was a sweet little voice in a huge clumsy body. I felt ashamed. Was I judging her because of her looks or was I picking something up?

That night in my dream I am going to an exorcism meeting, but something very powerful is trying to stop me. I feel like I am fighting against a very strong wind and I have to growl and roar to move forward, little by little. I eventually get to the meeting but there are a lot of people there that I am not happy about – they are just there for a thrill. A few of the genuine healers and I leave to conduct our own meeting. One healer says we should concentrate on a sound or a colour.

"Purple," I say and they all agree.

The healer who seems to be in charge touches my throat as if tracing something and this feels important. However, I wake from this dream in the early hours and I am panicky. I *see* something black, like a bundle of black clothes that slithers into my skull and slides around the back of my head. Panic grows. I don't like this black bundle, this thing, invading my head. It makes me think of the French girl who had been all in black, then, when I think of her, this black 'thing' quickly slithers, from the right hand side to the base of my skull. I shake my head. I cry out in panic. Help me! Over and over again it happens. I shudder and feel disgust. I try hard to relax and send light. Then I realize that I cannot have this girl share my home and once I decide on that I feel a little better and manage some sleep. I call her the next morning and tell her I'm sorry, but I have changed my mind.

What was going on? Was this just a panic reaction to sharing my home or did she leave behind a presence? If so, has it gone? At that moment I couldn't explain.

A few days later I feel the need to journey. I look at the layers of my subtle bodies after Flash has helped me out of the top of my head. The spiritual level is clear and bright, the causal full of loving presence, encouraging me. The Soul pulls at my throat. The emotional and mental seem ok, although the astral feels sticky. The Soul is the one I need to look at, so I ask Flash to come with me and immediately we are transported to a terrifying scene where I see myself in chains – arms crucified, feet chained and I am pinned there by two black-clad creatures (not humans). In front of me is a man in black who has torn out my throat and is holding it, laughing, mocking me. I feel fury. Rage rises inside me and overflows like lava spewing from a volcano. I will not let him have my power. Mentally, I scream at him, "You will not have my power. Give me back my power." My light is very strong and I turn the full force of it on him. His strength is diminishing. I tell him what a poor creature he is, eternally damned, eternally stuck in this place of hell, death and darkness.

"Give me back my power and I will help you heal," I say. "I am strong. Give me back all of the light you have stolen. Put it back here." And I point to a hole in the ground. "You can be healed. You can go to a place of healing," I tell him. The light starts to grow and grow in the hole and, at the same time, he gets smaller and smaller until he is only a bundle of black rags (Aha! Just like the one in my skull) and he is lifted off by the light. There are other souls around in the darkness, all of whom had been robbed of their light by this soul robber and I tell them, "Gather around the light. Take back what was yours and then you can move on." They do this.

I keep breathing my own power and light back into my throat centre. The soul robber had been threatened by my voice and power to speak against him. He had stolen my voice, but did not get my light.

Flash helped me fly back to the outer circle of my soul level and I moved down to my physical, bringing the light with me. My throat and lungs seemed hollow, so I filled them with light, the light of love, the light of my eternal soul, the light of understanding and compassion and forgiveness. I bring back the words "Take control. Take control of your life".

This journey was more of a spirit rescue and the French girl was the catalyst. Did she bring an entity with her? I feel she did. Of course, over-imagination must be guarded against even though I am not prone to hysteria. I hope by healing the soul robber that she too received the light.

Fortunately, the next few journeys tell me to relax, and that everything is being taken care of.

20

"To walk a daily path with love in your heart," are the words that I hear. What was that? A commandment? At first I thought, *That simple, huh?* But then again, is it?

I thought of other 'spiritual' sayings, which are all 'simple', yet not so. We can make it simple or we can make it difficult. We can struggle or we can ease along.

"There is nothing to fear."	Simple
"Love is all there is."	Simple
"Abundance is yours."	Simple
"Ask and ye shall receive."	Simple
"Love thy neighbour."	Simple

It's all so simple – love, kindness, abundance, sharing. We make it difficult. I make it difficult. *Imagine it is easy, Carol.* I groove along quite nicely with this thought till I consider the creatures from the swamp next door. Oh! Oh! Even them! I'm gonna have to work with this thought.

My first commandment – To walk a daily path with love in my heart.

Feels good. Thank you.

Ready to Commit

Almost a year after meeting Hannah and the Sisters I note that I have started affirming that 'It is Time'. I want to be dedicated to service, to Knowledge and Wisdom. I have been working with the Love Commandment and I sit to meditate at noon, my time for communing with White Eagle Lodge Healers, when the message, 'With love in our hearts may we hold the world in light', is sent out. I wonder how much more work I have to do with love before I can meet my wisdom teacher again and… Whoof!

I'm off in a little boat across a short stretch of water to an island, to a cave-like dwelling where I am reunited with Hannah or *Mother*. She is a beautiful woman in long robes and head covering, not unlike a nun, but full of light and shimmering colours. She welcomes me and I say, "I am ready now if you will still have me."

She points to a curtained area where there is a large bed, desk and chair. She says nothing but smiles as if obviously they have kept this space for me. My sisters are all smiling and I feel very welcome.

As I stood facing 'Mother' I thought she was going to put her hand on me, a blessing, but instead my body of light shot upwards in a long thin bright light that kept on travelling. Eventually, it curved forward, like an arc, but then started coiling, tighter and tighter, until the coil came close and entered my throat, filled my throat centre, expanded and gently vibrated. The mother also blew into my throat centre.

"It must be made clear," she said. "The wisdom of the heart must be able to move up and the wisdom of the insight must be able to move down, to be expressed, otherwise there is no point."

All my sisters were gathered around and I felt the first stirrings of love for them. I was aware that I had never felt sisterhood before – never really trusted women friends entirely – so I felt excited about building up love and trust.

A week or so later, I couldn't sleep one night and had a strong urge to sit up and meditate. I immediately set off in a little boat across the short stretch of water to the island of my sisters. Mother was waiting on the pebbly shore dressed in dark blue robes, as dark as the night. She greeted me warmly, embraced me and said, "We need you for healing."

I was puzzled. *Needed me?* Why would all this wisdom need me?

Someone was lying on a high table and it appeared to be one of the sisters. Again, I was perplexed – why would they get sick? The sisters stood around the table and smiled encouragingly at me. I really didn't understand, but I put my left hand on the brow of the sick woman and my right hand on her navel to run the energy through. This didn't feel right, so I went around the other side and put my right hand on her brow and my left on her navel. I tried to *see* what was wrong. I sensed a small clot just to the right of her nose, at the back of her eyebrow. I scanned the rest of her body and sensed that her uterus was absolutely rotten beyond repair. Again, I was puzzled. What could I do? My right hand moved to her navel and my left to the infected area and suddenly my left hand slid through skin and muscles, entering her body easier than through melted butter, and I just lifted out the rotten uterus. Someone appeared with a bucket and I put the uterus in it. I was then concerned about the spread of cancer still inside and I started to 'laser beam' with my mind and I noticed that all the sisters were doing the same. Mother signalled to me that the sisters would complete the clearing in this way.

I felt shocked at what had happened, but Mother said, "That's why we needed you to come – to show you what you can do."

"But, do I just do this in meditation or in real life?" I wanted to know.

The mother replied, "First in meditation, or mentally, until you gain confidence."

I told her that I am still shocked, but willing to do this work – any work. Willing and privileged.

*　*　*

Following on from this meditation, I have had strong urges to let my fingers penetrate the flesh, but this has not, in reality, happened. I have been visiting a stroke victim to give healing and now, when I go to him, I put my hands *on* his head and imagine my fingers penetrating and mending his fuses.

More weeks go past before I have a strong need to visit the mother and I go quickly and throw myself into her arms. She leads me to my sisters and I soak in their love. I sit at my desk as I have been given a huge book, which I lovingly caress. It then occurs to me that the sisters are not just sitting around reading, but are actually still setting down wisdom on the pages as well as learning wisdom to pass on to the earthly plane, as and when it is requested – like channels.

"Wisdom is only useful if it is being used," I hear.

I open my book and slowly a picture emerges of a woman sitting, seemingly passive, in a green forest-like setting, her back to a tree and with tumbling greenery all around. I sense she is full of wisdom and is 'holding the world in light' (the words White Eagle Lodge use).. I wonder if my next commandment is here…

My second commandment: To walk a daily path in full consciousness.

I sense I am being shown the power of knowing.

"Knowing that quietly we do good work. Women have the light to balance the world. Be in consciousness of this. Be in consciousness of what you can do for the world just being and knowing. Hold the light in your heart." This is what I sense from my book. The wisdom in my book is not in words. Is it the same for the other sisters? Is this our way to learn wisdom? Sense and experience? We must feel the wisdom in a deep place of understanding before we can pass on the concept in words appropriate to the person in need.

I thank everybody and rush back to 'reality' to write it all down.

A third commandment took many months to appear and was prompted by taking Findhorn Essences, which are like Bach Flower remedies. I intuitively chose 'Life Force' and 'Prosperity'. At first, interestingly, I felt I couldn't deal with 'Prosperity', felt panic even. Strange, I thought. So, I took 'Life Force' drops for a few days till I felt ok about 'Prosperity'.

On the morning of taking two doses of 'Prosperity', I sit to meditate and the word 'prosperity' filters into my mind and so I mull it over. Then I hear, "PRO SPIRITY". Of course! Revelation! ProSPIRIT, with Spirit, for Spirit. Then I had a lovely sense of what prosperity is. The light expanded around me. My heart opened and I breathed a sigh of release. Tension left my body. As usual, it's so simple when you get the drift! Everything I do, I do with Spirit. The only thing blocking abundance is me.

I felt a sense of gratitude coming back to me that I had lost. I felt the light again that I had lost contact with too. Whatever we do, if we do it with Spirit, we are in abundance.

My third commandment: Walk a daily path with Spirit and be in abundance.

Right then I felt as if prosperity was flowing through my veins. Prosperity is a state of heart and who better to confirm this than Lakshmi, the goddess of prosperity. As I feel a desire to sit quietly and still my chatter, she appears to me dressed very simply in pale blue and cream. She smiles at me and sits cross-legged. She seems very sensuous. Not fat at all, but voluptuous – an attitude maybe rather than a shape. People start approaching her and I see her smile with genuine love and gratitude as, one after another, they give her presents and drape her open arms with strings of jewels.

"Accept," she keeps telling me. "There is grace in acceptance."

She was completely unattached to these gifts; her lesson was in acceptance with Grace. "If the Universe gives, accept. There is no need to feel guilty if you accept love or abundance from others. It is not your lesson to give – it is theirs. Your lesson is to accept." She had obviously read my mind.

She was showing how you can give to others by accepting their gifts, but in accepting you do not become attached. Otherwise, there is no grace for you or for others. Such quietness, humility and gentleness came from her in the midst of all the gold and jewels.

21

Always, still, seeking solutions to my health challenges, I try various homoeopathic remedies. My friend Maureen Lockhart prescribes Stannum (Tin) and after taking it for a few days I respond with anger. Well, rage actually, together with lots of vibration at my throat and upper chest. I feel tired, disoriented (nothing new there) and have blocked-up sinuses then a sudden migraine-like attack with flashing lights and blind spots, headache and nausea.

The following day I felt better, up until I got into bed at night when I felt a crushing weight approaching and moving down towards the top of my head. I also had a crushing sensation on my scalp and temples then a feeling of being pinched on my eyebrows and more crushing on my cheekbones. Pains, weight, tugs all around. I felt as if my face was being rearranged. The pains moved swiftly: a huge flash of pain down my back and my left-hand side. Inside my head, as I tried to see, it seemed as if I was having lightning flashes and I heard myself say that there was a storm going on in my body. Strange goings-on, but eventually I fell asleep.

Next day, tired and worn out, I sat to meditate and to check out my aura. At the astral level there were huge swirling storm clouds with flashes of lightning and a tornado seemed to be approaching from the left. As I moved to look at the mental level, I felt a familiar tug at my throat, which I tried to follow, and felt myself falling....

My face moved. My upper teeth pushed out like buck

teeth. My chin fell back and I 'saw' a little Chinese man with a black string moustache. I felt it tickle my face. He was wearing a long brocade jacket and a little round hat with a black tassel. I heard myself say, "Master Chan," then I argued with myself as Chan was the name of the dragon I had already met.

Was he here as a new guide?

I ask him about my client who has had a stroke and he shows me where to place my fingers (three fingers: one on top of the head and two at the base of the skull on the left) demonstrating by actually putting in needles. I ask if he can help me; he puts needles in various places on my face and head and leaves them there for a while before slowly receding and I return to normal – normal?!

All is quiet for a few days. I sit to meditate and feel a strong pull that tugs at my throat and tells me we are going somewhere. I see no pictures, but there is a sense of beautiful connection. I place my hands on my upper chest where I understand the immune system is located and I sense that this is the 'love thyself' centre. Of course. A poor immune system could not fully love oneself. I hear again the words of Michael – "Thou must believe in thee" – and I am filled with feelings of love. My upper chest feels as if it has cracked open and the love and light pour forth. I see with clarity the beautiful inner light that is my essence. I see the 'reality' of what I am and it is stunning. My inner eternal essence. It is so beautiful. Shiny iridescent little fluttering creatures burst out.

"Spread love around," I hear.

Why do we hide this light? I feel now, what I already accepted intellectually, that if you love yourself, as I have just felt, how much easier to let that love and light pour over and touch others.

If you learn to forgive yourself you can forgive others. The same with acceptance; once you reach self love, you can love others with a heart fit to burst!

It stuns me sometimes how long it can take for my intellect to reach my heart.

But back to homoeopathy, which, in the hands of a good practitioner, can be miraculous, and Maureen is an excellent one. She introduces me to the new remedies of colour and gem stones and they interest me immensely. With most forms of healing I feel that faster and higher vibrations are needed. I have been feeling a desperate need for the colour Turquoise, so needy that I found myself sucking on a scarf which had some turquoise in it. Maureen sent me a Turquoise Remedy and after four days fantastic dreams began. They were about fun and laughter, letting go, moving on. Full of detail. I also became very sensitive. I had a meal with MSG in it and I had a complete loss of energy, like a cartoon character that had been steamrollered and I slid off the chair.

I started craving orange, again with desperation, my eyes seeking it out everywhere. I visited a cousin who had a Siamese cat and I had a strong allergic reaction, looking as if I had been in a fight, my eyes puffy and bruised and I wheezed and whistled.

When I meditate I meet a beautiful mermaid and see such wonderful colour: blue/green scales of the mermaid's tail, her long golden curls.

"Let go! Let go! Let go!" she says.

I dream about colour – glorious pale iridescent colours – and I see what looks like finely-quilted material of white, but it is luminous with pinks and lilacs. It seemed that these colours were made of the tiniest (subatomic) particles, and that is why they shimmered making it impossible to say exactly what the colours were. These were the particles of colour that we don't normally see. They are to be used to heal the subatomic particles, the 'spaces' inside human beings and all beings. The colours usually used in healing are no longer subtle enough for subatomic and the subtle bodies. We are vibrating at higher speeds and these new colours are now needed for deep healing. I was shown the new colours then the old ones to see the difference. I asked if I could use these new colours now, on myself and they felt absolutely glorious. I felt as if all my cells, atoms and the spaces in between were bathed in this indescribable colour.

I have had a very busy time with dreams, meditations and healings, which led me to meeting The Venetian Master, Paul Verinisi, who is apparently the master who works with the new pastel colours coming in for the planet. Ah ha! I see him clearly, a handsome, cavalier type with blonde hair, twinkling blue eyes and a little beard. Two or three times a day I meet with him and ask for his colours. He is a delightful presence. I ask him to be present while I am giving healing and there is a different texture somehow.

A Visit to the Hall of Wisdom

What a lucky girl am I. But, just when I thought it was safe to go back in the water, a huge cosmic slap sets off all my health problems and I feel unwell, overwhelmed, drowning. I have a feverish need to write all of it out of my system. Where is the key to it all? There must be a key. I want to sick it out, vomit away my health problems. Mucous, diarrhoea, cough, fatigue, vomit, vomit, vomit. So sick am I of it all.

Questions I ask – no answers. Everything I try – no remedy. Here we go again. Am I not good enough? Is it in my stars? Is it my karma, my destiny, my life lessons? This is why I write; write it out of my life!

My pencil scrapes page after page until I run out of steam and sit to meditate, though it still takes a while to settle with all my mutterings. I yell at the chaps upstairs that I'm fed up. I want to hear a clear voice that gives me answers. I want a recipe. I want a huge flash of lightning and a booming voice saying, "Wear sensible shoes and warm knickers in winter and YOU WILL BE WELL." That's what I want. Not all this stuff about being patient. "Bollocks to patience!" I yell.

I sit in a huff, but soon I follow the 'falling through space' feeling and find myself sitting in a corridor in front of two huge wooden doors. Still a bit huffy, I think to myself, *Huh, I'll probably be kept waiting.* But no; both doors open and I see an elderly man then to his left a beautiful woman appears and invites me to enter. Well, what I enter is the most wonderful space, floor-to-ceiling with books. Old carved wood, stained glass windows and books. I could smell the books and there are people on the gallery level, reading and writing at small desks. The woman explains to me that this is the hall of wisdom and that wisdom is still being written. She tells me I can choose a book or just browse. Whatever I want. I can't really think of a particular subject and I don't know where to start, but I think of the question, "What is the Plan?" I sense that it will take more than one book to answer that, so I slowly walk around close to the books, hoping for inspiration. As I walk, I *hear* that the books sing. I listen and I hear them murmur pleasantly, like a vibration. I hear one with a different, compelling voice so I stop and try to remove it from the shelf. I pull it, but it won't budge. I try again, but no. I hear the word "persistence", so I pull harder. The book starts to move, but I decide that I don't want a book that is about persistence by force and I let it go. I think about persistence by love and the book glides smoothly out. I look at its spine which says, 'Persistence through Love by Carol Ann Deans'!

22

I meet an Indian man. He is filing large leaves into pigeon-holes. I ask for his help and he asks my name and checks my karmic records. He sighs and looks at me very kindly and says, "One last thing to be done. You must face the demon."

I say, "ok," and feel glad to be doing this.

He tells me that I have to go to a very, very deep and dark place. Flash is with me and we fall down, down, down into a dark tunnel where we see other tunnels running off in all directions. It is cold and damp. Everywhere there are dark tortured beings – lost souls grasping, hissing, spitting and clawing at us as we pass by. I am not afraid. I feel only compassion. I have not yet seen my demon, but I 'heard' that this is where the 'banished souls' were.

A dark shadow starts to manifest and grow in front of me, till it appears as a rotting, maggoty face – black cloak all around, snakes and spitting things shoot in and out and I am reminded of the heads of Kali. I still feel no fear. I stand my ground. At first I feel that this dark being needs forgiveness, but when I offer this it responds with fury. I wonder whether it needs to forgive me. It takes a while for the story to unfold, but it seems that this 'demon' is the part of me that was banished a very, very long time ago. Why?

In my inner vision I am shown the life I had in an Indian temple and see that this dark being in front of me now had been banished so that I would be a pure white vestal virgin for the temple. I had been a temple prostitute. I was eighteen years old. I have seen glimpses of this life before and the huge sadness that I felt in that lifetime. I then realize that I did not banish that part of me. It was Him – that black disgusting thing that had ripped out my voice box at another time. He had banished that part of me that had been my independence, my spark, the bit that rebelled and caused him inconvenience. It was not my darkness that was sent away; it was my light. That dark malevolent being and I had history! Now was the time to be done with him. Forever.

Back in the deep dark place, I retrieve that banished part of myself who is very hurt. I eventually persuade her to come back to me once I tell her the story and tell her I love her and want her to be part of me again. She agrees and wants to be with me now so that together we can face Him. That cloak of darkness disappears as love and light are shared. We are together now and we are powerful.

The black malevolence appears in front of me and he is furious. He rages and roars, but I will not be diminished. Flash stands firm by my side. Other light beings come to help me. They want to take him with them to the light, but he is screaming obscenities, spitting, struggling and panicking. With the force of the light he is at last detached from me and I feel his panic. I want to throw up. My stomach heaves and I am gagging. After a huge struggle the angels are comforting him and listening to his story. Even malevolent beings have a story. He then starts shrinking and allows himself to be taken to the light, but not before I insist we look into each other's eyes and, as we do, only compassion remains. It is over.

This was a 'soul retrieval' that a friend and healing colleague, Linda Evans, helped me with. A couple of smaller things also needed attending to and sending on their way, but this was small fry compared to what we had just dealt with. Following this, Linda gave me a lovely healing and I was able to breathe more easily and then Archangel Michael appeared to me and offered me the missing key. I took it and placed it on my chest, between heart and throat centre. The key is truthfulness. The only door that needs to be opened is the door to my heart. All is contained therein. Nothing is separate or separated.

I sleep deeply and dream peacefully that night, and for many nights thereafter.

Could it be that I have no more demons to face? Fluttering fearful small things? I have travelled a long way on my personal journey. Where am I now? What questions have I answered? What was it I set out to do?

I understand that my journey started because of ill health and that the journey continued because of the struggle to find answers, beating my anguished breast, feeling useless, abandoned and not seeing lessons.

A Course in Miracles says, "Illness is some form of external searching," and also, "Health is inner peace."

The working title for this book has always been, *Writing Myself Well*. I hoped that by continually clearing myself out, I would eventually be sparkling new and physically splendid. In reality, this has not quite happened. How then can I write a happy conclusion? I always love a happy ending after all.

If I have not written myself well then what have I written and where am I on this healing journey? What is healing anyway? Am I still expecting a miracle of biblical proportion? Would be nice. I don't think I'll ever entirely let go of that, but what I have found is more precious. I have found myself.

If healing is appreciating all of who I am then I am healed. If healing is happiness and a strong loving heart I am healed. Emotional health and a strong mental body? Well, hallelujah! For I am healed. I am at one with my Soul, open to spiritual dimensions and I believe I have found that inner peace. I am blessed and I know I will live happily ever after.

Every life is a quest – a hero's journey – and, like the labours of Hercules, we are all given obstacles to overcome. We need to be brave and have our wits about us. We are all heroes no matter how insignificant we may feel, and if we pick up a pen and write that journey becomes clearer. We prove that we have lived. We can see with our own eyes, written in black and white. We have conquered. We have overcome. We are not useless. If we go inside ourselves and write our story we can see how brave and wise and magical we truly are.

There is an old Turkish proverb, which says, 'The road is never long with good companions'. I can attest to that. I am excited and ready to continue on my quest, wondering who I will next meet and where I will journey. I'm pretty sure it won't be boring.

Appendix

Just in case you are new to the subjects, I thought a few ideas and suggestions for creative visualization and meditation might be helpful. There are many excellent books on the market, for all levels, and these are just some basic ideas to get you started.

Set the Scene

Choose a time and a place where you will not be disturbed for at least half an hour or so. You may like to light a candle. If you have soft atmospheric music that soothes, you could put that on, or you may prefer to sit quietly. Try one way, then the other and see which feels most comfortable. As your body relaxes deeply you might feel a bit chilled, so a blanket around you or within reach is a good idea. I like to keep a notebook and pencil beside me in case I want to anchor some inspired idea. I am accustomed to sitting upright in a chair, feet flat on the floor and hands on my lap. No crossing of legs or arms.

Some people prefer to sit cross-legged on the floor, yoga style, but that is a strain for me. It is ok to sit cross-legged in this way as the base of your body is attaching you to earth. If lying in bed is the only way you can do this then that is ok too, although it is difficult to stay awake. Wherever and whenever is best for you is the main thing. Nothing is written in stone.

What I did find useful in the early days of meditation

practice was the habit of always lighting a candle, always wrapping myself in the same blanket, sitting in the same chair and trying to sit at the same time every day. It becomes a trigger, like Pavlov's Dogs, and that meditative state of mind is more easily reached.

If you can manage a few stretching exercises first it will help you relax your muscles. Then, we are off.

Relaxation

So, in your most comfortable setting, close your eyes and be aware of the breath entering and leaving your body. Through your nose, on the in-breath, feel the cool air entering your nostrils, then the warm air as it leaves on the out-breath. Sit for a few moments just observing how this feels. Slow your breathing to a comfortable rate then imagine your feet firmly attached to the ground, as if they had grown roots and dug down. Allow them to feel warm and relaxed, happy to move this warmth up your legs, one leg at a time, little by little to your knees, then upwards, to the top of your thighs. Allow your buttocks to sink into the chair…

Feel the muscles in your belly relax, allowing your breath to slow even more; direct your thoughts to your back, feeling as if bright sunlight is lingering there, working up your spine, one vertebra at a time, then spreading outwards to soften the muscles across your back. When you reach your shoulders, notice how they drop as all the tension you may be holding there falls away, runs down your arms, your hands and out through your fingers and gone.

Focus on the back of your neck, feeling that warm sun caressing up and over your head to your face. Imagine your temples are being lovingly massaged and as the tension leaves, your jaw will want to drop slightly and your tongue loll back inside your mouth. Behind your ears there are muscles that become very stressed and tight. Imagine your calm soft breath washing over this tension and as you let go, any little lines on your forehead and your face will smooth away, your eyelids relax, and your cheekbones melt.

If you are still aware of any remaining tension, consciously return to it and let it go.

Maintain this peaceful state for as long as you feel able. The goal is to reach 'stillness of mind' and once you reach this state you can choose your thoughts. You will come to realize what a cacophony of noisy tumbling thoughts there are in your mind and you will appreciate the lull of slowing it all down and gently dismissing the irrelevant ones. Treat these like a child demanding attention.

"Yes, ok. I hear you and I'll listen to you later."

A demanding child rarely agrees first time, so be prepared to gently but firmly repeat, "I hear you and I'll think about it soon. I'm busy right now." Or words to that effect. No point getting irritated or that child will start stamping its feet! Be patient. Sometimes I see myself taking hold of that irritating thought in my hand and placing it on one side to deal with later. If a thought continually arises then allow it to speak to you and if it seems worth contemplating, go ahead; otherwise, let it go and return to the centre of your still being.

One way of maintaining a peaceful state is to count each in breath, from one to ten. If you become distracted, or drift off for a while, just go back and start again at number one. Don't get frustrated with yourself. Repeat this procedure each time you want to meditate or visualize and it becomes easier and easier.

From here your mind will help you find all the states you need: joy, serenity, inner strength, courage. In my experience, if I achieve serenity, joy is never far behind and if I feel serene and joyful, well, everything else is possible or rendered unnecessary.

147

Visualization

When you have completed your relaxation exercise and feel ready…

I want you to imagine you are in a beautiful garden full of flowers. Feel a gentle breeze on your face. Hear the buzzing of the insects as they flit from flower to flower; the birds singing happy songs. See the colours of the flowers, hot reds, vibrant orange and smell the freshly cut grass under your feet. You may want to sit a while admiring the colours and enjoying the warm sun. Above, the sky is clear blue and the feeling is of complete tranquillity.

Then, as you continue to stroll in the garden, you come to a little gate. Lift the latch and walk through into a beautiful meadow of lush grass and wild flowers. You see an old oak tree with wide spread arms just a little further on. When you reach there you sit under the tree, your back against its strong trunk. The sun is shining, warm but gentle through the leaves, making you feel so sleepy and more and more relaxed. Close your eyes and allow yourself to drift off…

So, this is the introduction and you may find it useful to practise these first two stages before proceeding with your desired journey or question.

At this point I would like to explain something of the symbols and colours used. The reason I like to start by walking through a garden looking at flowers is that the colours of all the flowers have a meaning, which I will come to shortly. I like to 'open the gate' because it is symbolic of going down through the layers of consciousness. I then go into the meadow because it makes me feel like tumbling and running and very joyous. The old oak tree feels strong and protective. In my 'serenity' meditation, which I will share with you, I go to a high mountainous plateau. The plateau gives me security as I am prone to vertigo. There, my feet are firmly on ground but my vision is on high, far-seeing. The lake is calmness and the lotus is the symbol of the jewel of the mind. A large bird represents utter freedom. A little bird singing is joyful and clear-voiced. I don't go for snowy scenes as I prefer warmth. The list of symbols is as infinite as the possibilities of your mind.

Using Visualization to Find Answers

I like to go through the garden and into the meadow, sitting myself under the oak tree before I ask to meet someone for advice. Under the tree I feel deeply relaxed though grounded and protected. I can then focus on my question, which should be clear and precise.

Who do you want to meet?

What question do you want to ask?

If you are not too sure who it is you want to meet, ask, "Who is it most important for me to meet today?"

Wait till you see someone walking towards you. Notice what they look like.

Do you like their presence? If not, send them away, calmly and firmly.

You could ask to meet your spirit guide or your inner healer. You could ask for the archetype of courage or wisdom to appear to you and once they are with you, ask your question. Hear their answer. Thank them and if you would like to meet them again, ask if this would be possible. Go with the flow. When you feel ready, walk back through the meadow, the garden, and back to your body in present time. Give yourself a good stretch, wriggle your toes and rub your legs to ensure you are feeling awake.

I'm feeling a bit envious as you have all this still to explore! Just have fun and follow your intuition. There are so many how-to books and workshops, etc. But nothing is written in stone. No one way is the only way and at the risk of being a bore, I repeat, follow your own intuition. Try out as many ways as you want and if one feels as if you're wearing an old and comfy sweater then that's one to keep. Conversely, if it feels stiff and ill-fitting let it go. Also, use all of your senses when 'visualizing'. If you strain to 'see' pictures inside your head, you may end up with a headache. A sense of smell is wonderfully evocative as is feeling a breeze on your skin or taking off your shoes and walking on the warm grass or allowing sand at the beach to squidge through your toes. All this helps to create an atmosphere.

Using Colour in Visualization

Incorporating colours and symbols into your visualization is self-healing. For example, as I already mentioned, I include coloured flowers and green grass and these are just some of the reasons:

RED: a bright clear red, like poppies, is uplifting and life-enhancing, especially if you are feeling dull and listless.

ORANGE: energetic, cheering and warming. It is better for arthritic joints than red and is also good for the digestion.

YELLOW: imagine a bright glowing yellow that reflects sunshine and joy. If you are feeling depressed or 'blue', yellow will lift the emotions.

These first three colours are usually also associated with the lower centres of the body.

GREEN: the colour of balance. The green of nature brings peace and feelings of liberation. If you ever feel the need to fill your lungs with clean air, think green and wide open spaces. This colour corresponds with the heart centre, which is the body's balancer, being midway between the lower and more physical centres and the mental and aspirational centres.

LIGHT BLUE: tranquillity of clear blue waters or azure sky gives emotional clarity, openness and corresponds with the throat centre, which works well when it has a clear voice and truth.

DEEP BLUE: for nourishment, comfort and growth. I like to wrap myself in this colour, which corresponds with inner sight, the third eye and encourages the thought processes and contemplation.

LILAC and PURPLE: these are the colours of spiritual aspiration when we seek to elevate the mind. Lilac is a cleansing colour and has been referred to as 'spiritual disinfectant'. It is often used in healing, like a laser. Purple is also very healing.

Two other colours that are important to me are ROSE PINK, the colour of love, and GOLD, the highest we can achieve. I should also mention that BLACK is the absence of colour and WHITE contains all the colours of the spectrum.

Most of what we need is contained therein and we can consciously include these colours in visualizations and meditations or we can wait to see if these colours arise of their own accord, perhaps to show us something.

There are many excellent books to help you explore colour more deeply and also to explain the energy centres, or chakras. I can recommend Ruth White's *Working with your Chakras*, which is informative and easy to understand.

Serenity Meditation

My mind takes me to a high plateau in a mountain range, which I feel is in the Andes. (Incidentally, I don't bother visualizing an arduous climb; I just GO.)

The wind is chill and strong, though in the clear dazzlingly blue sky the sun burns relentlessly. I shelter in the mouth of a shallow cave and while I sit and contemplate the grandeur of my surroundings I calm my breath and relax, allowing peace to descend. I always seem to be wearing robes of deep wine colour trimmed with saffron yellow. I also appear to be comfortable sitting cross-legged.

There are a few scrubby little plants clinging tenaciously to the rocks. Perhaps they feel, like me, the battle to be here is worthwhile, to view the vastness, the uninterrupted glory of nature, to contemplate our place in the great scheme of things and to realize that dull and scrubby we may be, but we are still part of it all. The howl and occasional 'whoo' of the wind is the only sound until I hear the distinctive call of a condor and see its great wings swoop up and down on the thermals. My heart swells with overwhelming joy, making me feel like jumping to my feet, outstretching my arms and yelling loud and long with the bursting gladness of being alive.

Returning to calm, I direct my gaze to the small mountain lake that shares this plateau. Its clear sparkling water remains calm despite the wind. In the middle there is a lotus flower of cream and pink with deeper pink at its tips. As I sit gazing, a feeling of serenity overtakes calm and peace, and I am bathed in colours that reflect the lotus. Slowly, the petals of the lotus begin to unfold, tempting me to remain focused until it shows its heart of peach and gold. I gladly unfold my heart in return and feel myself serenely float away...

Bespoke Journeys

Perhaps, for you, a snowy mountain top may transport you to peace, or a tropical island to feel deep rest and tranquillity. The beauty of journeying in the mind is you don't need a travel agent or to sit for hours on an aeroplane with your knees under your chin! Just follow your thoughts. A point to remember is not to put yourself in a scary position, like in the middle of an ocean where a storm could suddenly whip up. Better to be on a cushion-lined punt on a tranquil lake where you can completely let go knowing there are boundaries.

Another use for 'taking off' is when you find yourself in a situation you would rather not be in (for example, the dentist's chair). I was reminded of this recently while undergoing root canal work. I was trying to relax my body, but was so aware of that whirr of the drill, which I dislike intensely. Suddenly, I thought, *Carol, get yourself out of here. Somewhere nicer,* and off I went. My old friend Flash came with me and we settled in a little cove of a large lake. The clear sparkling water chuckled across the pebbly shore and was so enticing I pulled my clothes off and waded in, gasping and laughing with sheer joy.

"C'mon Flash," I yelled. "Get your clothes off." But he wouldn't do that. Just plain refused. Wouldn't even take off his big silver boots. I teased him at his shyness as I swam and floated in complete peace.

I imagined little creatures coming to drink and, one by one, all sorts of animals appeared. Some shy, some bold. I imagined (then saw) birds and animals from every far-flung place in the world. Flash and I sat on a rock for a while enjoying the sun, then back I would go into the soothing water ...

When the dentist said, one hour later, that he was finished, I was still smiling behind my eyes and my body was tension-free.

Recording Your Dreams

I used to laboriously record my dreams, which always seemed to be a long whinge of disconnected incidents that I never could bring together or come to any conclusion as to their meaning. It became a chore and a bore until I attended a workshop where extremely useful tips were given, which I will now share.

At the workshop, the facilitator asked us if anyone had had a significant dream the night before. One brave young woman raised a hand and she was asked to tell us the dream. We all listened intently, hoping that we would be able to pull out some insight, which we couldn't. Maybe one or two details stuck. The facilitator thanked the young woman and asked her if she would mind telling the dream again. The young woman, puzzled, did so and we noted that some of the descriptions were missing, some of the fripperies, but we still did not really find any great meaning. The facilitator then thanked the young woman, but then asked if she wouldn't mind telling the dream again. The young woman was a little irritated, but took a deep breath and rattled through the telling of the dream, leaving out all the extraneous details. She told only the salient parts and – whaddya know? – we all got it. We all lit up with comprehension. In the paring down and paring down she had sloughed off all the dross that was getting in the way of the meaning, which now shone out, seeking resolution. We all clapped and cheered as we realized that when you dream it is *your* dream, *your* subconscious and *your* Answers. You don't have to resort to books of meanings or to another person for illumination. You can do it yourself, especially with these other hints:

Firstly, give your dream a title. Right away that cuts to the chase and sums it up.

Secondly, explore how the dream made you feel. Was it a dream of fear, shame, love, etc? Did it leave you feeling terrified, lost, enchanted?

Thirdly, identify the characters. Who was in the dream and what is their relevance to you? Was it an authority figure, parent, object of desire?

Lastly, be aware of the setting. Was it in nature, which is more of a soul dream? Or was it in a city or a building of some sort, which is more of a personality dream?

When you have recorded the salient facts, you will come to some understanding of what may be troubling you and be able to get on with your day.

Smiling Meditation

When you feel 'down in the mouth', turn things around by smiling. This can be a tall order if you are depressed and just can't seem to find anything to cling onto to elevate you, but the first thing that happens when you smile is that your mouth turns up. Give it a try even if you don't really mean it at first.

Turn up your mouth in a smile. Relax the muscles in your face and let the smile linger. Your eyes will smile too. Allow the smile to move down inside your throat, then down inside your chest.

Your breath will slow and deepen as the smile moves further down. By the time your smile reaches your belly, all your muscles will let go as your body relaxes and your inner organs smile along with you.

Now, tell me you don't feel better.

Resources

National Federation of Spiritual Healers (NFSH)
The Healing Trust
21 York Road
Northampton
United Kingdom
NN1 SQG
Tel: +441604 603247
www.thehealingtrust.org.uk

White Eagle Lodge
Newlands
Brewells Lane
Hampshire
GU33 7HY
Tel: +44(0)730 893300
www.whiteagle.org

Foundation for Emotional Therapy
www.emotionaltherapy.co.uk

School for the Study of the Seven Rays
19611 Antioch Road
White City, Oregon
97503
USA
WEBSITE www.seven-rays.org E mail: lampus@wizzards.net

M.E. Association
www.meassociation.org.uk
ME Connect Helpline
Tel +44(0)8445765326

The College of Past Life Healing no longer exists in the UK as the founder, Diane Park (later known as Kiana Park), moved back to Australia. Some of the graduates may be found online.

Bibliography

Begg, Deike, *Rebirthing: Freedom from your Past* (Thorsons, 1999)

Cooper, Diana, *A Little Light on Ascension* (Findhorn Press, 1997)

De Rohan, Ceanne, *Original Cause* (Four Winds Publications, USA 1984)

Galloway, Janice, *The Trick is to Keep Breathing* (Minerva New Edition, 1991)

Goldberg, Natalie, *Writing Down the Bones* (Shambala Publications Inc., 1986)

Kenton, Leslie, *13 Quantum Leaps for the Soul* (Thorsons 2000)

Krishna, Gopi, *Living with Kundalini: The Autobiography of Gopi Krishna* (Shambala Dragon Editions 1993)

Krystal, Phyllis, *Cutting the Ties that Bind* (Red Wheel/Weiser, 1993)

Pinkola Estes, Clarisa, *Women Who Run With The Wolves* (Ballantine Books, 1992)

Tolle, Ekhart, *The Power of Now* (Hodder & Stoughton, 2001)

Unknown, *A Course in Miracles* (Foundation for Inner Peace)

Walsh, Neale Donald, *Conversations with God* (Hodder Mobius, 1997)

White Eagle, *Beautiful Road Home* (The White Eagle Publishing Trust, July 1992)

White, John, *Kundalini, Evolution and Enlightenment* (Paragon House Publishers, revised edition, April 1990)

Other Recommended Reading

Abraham, Kurt, Introduction to the *Seven Rays*; (1986) 'Achieving Quiet Mind' 2008 (Available through Lampus Press the Publishing House for School for the Study of Seven Rays (www.seven-rays.org (see Resources Page) or Amazon)

Bowman, Carol, *Children's Past Lives: How Past Life Memories Affect your Child (Element 1997)*

Brunton, Paul, *A Search in Secret India (first published by Rider 1934, latest edition by Random House, 2003)*

Grant, Joan, The *Far Memory* Book Series first printed in Great Britain 1939 Reprinted Overlook Duckworth 2007)

Lipton, Bruce, *The Biology of Belief (Hay House latest edition 2009)*

Maclaine, Shirley, *Out on a Limb (Bantum USA reissue 1987); Going Within a Guide for Inner Transformation (Bantum USA Reprint edition1990); The Camino: A Pilgrimage of Courage (Pocket Books new edition 2001)*

Mountaindreamer, Oriah, *The Call (published in Great Britain by Element 2003)*

Stanley Alder, Vera, *The Finding of the Third Eye (first published by Rider & Co London, 1938)*

Weiss, Brian L., *Many Lives, Many Masters (Piatkus Books 1994)*

White Eagle Publications: All of their publications are simply and clearly written (see Resources Page)

White, Ruth, *Working with your Chakras, Judy Piatkus (Publishers) Ltd 1993*